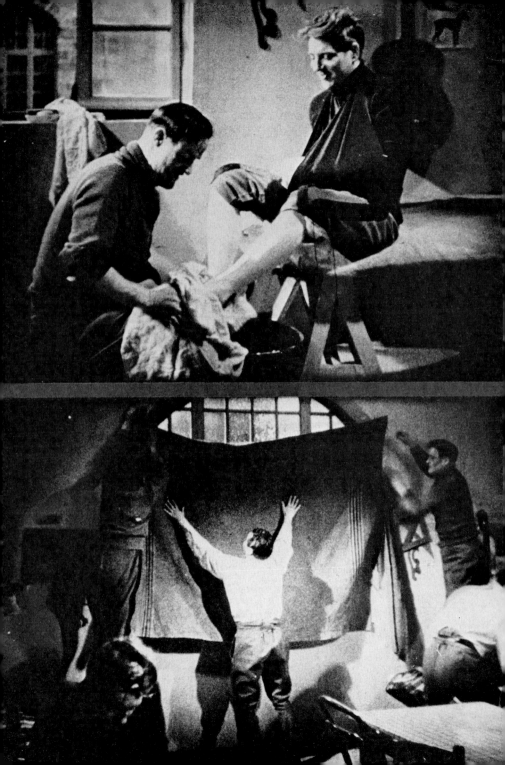

536419
film hist/R

GRAND ILLUSION
a film by
Jean Renoir

translated from the French
by Marianne Alexandre and Andrew Sinclair

Simon and Schuster, New York

General Editor: Sandra Wake

Stills by courtesy of l'Avant-Scène du Cinéma and the
British Film Institute
Frontispiece: Jean Renoir in 1924

Library of Congress Catalog Card Number: 68-21912

Manufactured in Great Britain by Villiers Publications Ltd.,
London N.W.5

CONTENTS

A NOTE FROM JEAN RENOIR

The story of *La Grande Illusion* is absolutely true and was told to me by some of my comrades in the war . . . I am obviously referring to the war of 1914. In 1914, Hitler had not yet appeared. Nor had the Nazis, who almost succeeded in making people forget that the Germans are also human beings. In 1914, men's spirits had not yet been warped by totalitarian religions and racism. In certain ways, that world war was still a war of formal people, of educated people — I would almost dare say, a gentlemen's war. That does not excuse it. Politeness, even chivalry, does not excuse massacre.

MY FIRST MEETING WITH JEAN RENOIR

Of all the film directors I have met in the course of my chequered career, I have admired a few and worshipped one. I worshipped D. W. Griffith the way that someone can worship the man who has taught him everything, who has lavished the treasures of genius on him without holding back. He was the greatest of his day; this is not a personal opinion, all those who ever worked for him agree with me. But there was another man for whom I felt, from the very first moment, an irresistible sympathy, and that was Jean Renoir.

I must admit that, before meeting him, I was on my guard; I had just had several unfortunate experiences with American colleagues, and had had to leave that country as well as give up my job.

There had already been a lot of repercussions, the result of petty jealousies or even full-scale hatreds. So I was very nervous at the prospect of meeting my future director. I waited for him in the partly-furnished office, where the company backing *La Grande Illusion* had arranged for us to meet. I heard footsteps in the corridor, the door opened. A heavily-built man in baggy clothing was standing in the doorway. I could not describe his face; I will only say that I was struck by his eyes. Not that they were beautiful, but that they were incredibly blue and sharp with intelligence. Before I knew it, he had walked up to me and had kissed me firmly on my cheeks. As a rule I am not overfond of such demonstrations of affection. In fact, I loathe even a handshake with a member of my own sex. Yet I returned this unexpected show of friendliness without the least hesitation.

Then, Renoir caught me by the shoulder and held me at arm's length to take a better look at me. Finally, never taking his eyes off me, he told me in German how much he liked my past work and how glad he was that I was going to work with him — he said ' with ' not ' for ' him. There was no need to beat about the bush; I understood that all would go well. The only thing that upset me was that I could not return his compliment, for, alas, I had not seen any of his films. But I warmly expressed my delight at working for him.

We began chatting and I noticed with pleasure that he was very familiar with my films; he even remembered some of them much more clearly than I did, recalling things in them that I had completely forgotten. But we were there mainly to talk about *La Grande Illusion* and the part I was going to play. I had been sent a first, hasty draft of the script which I had read, and — being incorrigible — I began making a few hesitant suggestions. Now that I knew what sort of man Jean Renoir was, I could speak up without fear. That man was incapable of taking offence at what more narrow-minded souls would have considered crimes of impertinence. I could talk to him as openly as to a brother, without hedging. And he was not stalling for time, waiting for a future opportunity to say more or less a veiled ' no ' to my overtures. He examined the subject we were discussing with an enthusiasm that brought tears to my eyes. He had given me a pleasure which I had forgotten for some years.

All the work I did with Renoir turned out to be as friendly as that first meeting. I have never met a man with greater self-control. I saw him at Upper Koenigsburg while he was shooting the most important scenes of *La Grande Illusion*. Everything seemed to be against him, even God, for it began to snow in the middle of a scene — it snowed for so long that Renoir had to change the film script in order to justify this untimely snowfall.

For five days and five nights, Renoir worked without a break. On the sixth day, the sun came out and, in less than an hour, the snow melted. An impressive amount of film was thus suddenly rendered useless. Renoir did not bat an eyelid. He calmly went about arranging for some plaster, naphthaline and boric acid to be sent over, then settled down to wait for its arrival.

He is incredibly patient. Without ever raising his voice, he asks over and over again until he gets what he wants. His politeness towards everyone he works with was a source of endless amazement to me, especially as I personally cannot say three words in succession without swearing in whatever language I am using.

Jean Renoir could have been an excellent diplomat as well, for he has more finesse and ability in his little finger than any professional has in what he calls his brains.

ERICH VON STROHEIM

CREDITS :

Scenario, adaptation and dialogue	Charles Spaak and Jean Renoir
Directed by	Jean Renoir
Produced by	Réalisations d'Art Cinémato-graphique (R.A.C.) (Frank Rollmer, Albert Pinkovitch and Alexandre)
Music	Joseph Kosma
Lyrics	Vincent Telly and A. Valsien
(Si tu veux, Marguerite . . .)	(as sung by Fragson)
Technical Advisor	Carl Koch
Assistant Director	Jacques Becker
1st Operator	Christian Matras
2nd Operator	Claude Renoir
Set Designer	Lourie
Sound Engineer	de Bretagne
Orchestra	Vuillermoz (arranged by Smyth)
Editor	Marguerite Marthe-Huguet

CAST :

von Rauffenstein	Erich von Stroheim
Maréchal	Jean Gabin
de Bœldieu	Pierre Fresnay
Rosenthal	Dalio
The Actor	Julien Carette
The Engineer	Gaston Modot
The Teacher	Jean Daste
French Soldier	Georges Peclet
English Officer	Jacques Becker
Demolder	Sylvain Itkine
Elsa	Dita Parlo
Others	W. Florian, C. Sainval, etc.

Shot during	Winter 1936-1937
Studios	Billancourt and Eclair
Locations	In Alsace, the outskirts of Neuf-Brisach, in Haut-Koenigsburg and the barracks of Colmar

11

GRAND ILLUSION

Titles: then the legend: THE EVENTS DESCRIBED IN THIS FILM TOOK PLACE DURING THE WAR OF 1914-1918.
In the officers' mess of an air squadron on the French front, camera tracks into close-up of a gramophone with a horn, playing the music of the song ' Frou-Frou, Frou-Frou . . .', also being hummed by a man's voice. Pan up to Lieutenant MARECHAL *who is bending over the gramophone as though hypnotized by the spinning record. He seems lost in distant memories, as he sings the chorus.*

MARECHAL *close-up* : Frou-Frou . . . Frou-Frou-Frou . . . Tra la la la . . . la . . . la . . . Frou-Frou . . .

MARECHAL *is a mechanic whom circumstance has made an officer. He is wearing a uniform, his képi pushed slightly towards the back of his head, his airman's jacket unbuttoned, his scarf loosely knotted round his neck. It is winter, one of the terrible winters of that war, and this officers' mess behind the French front is not very warm. Behind* MARECHAL *in a blurred background, a few officers are seen sitting at tables near the bar, talking together. Suddenly,* MARECHAL *snaps out of his reverie and lifts his head. Camera follows him towards the bar, where he speaks to a soldier,* HALPHEN.

MARECHAL : Hey! I say, waiter, are you going to Epernay?

HALPHEN : Yes, of course.

MARECHAL : When?

HALPHEN : In half-an-hour.

MARECHAL, *near him now* : In the lorry? HALPHEN *nods.* Well then, be a sport . . . try to wait for me.

HALPHEN : Joséphine.

MARECHAL, *as though it were obvious* : Well naturally . . . Joséphine.

HALPHEN *smiling* : You're not the only one.

MARECHAL *shrugging* : I don't care!

>*Pan towards the door, revealing the other officers talking and drinking together at different tables; the record plays the same song. Captain* RINGIS *bursts in. Camera pans back with him as he spots* MARECHAL *and goes over to speak with him.*

RINGIS : Hey, Maréchal . . . there's a fellow there from the General Staff. . . . You've got to show him around.

MARECHAL *disappointed* : A bloke from the General Staff? . . . Hmmm, well. . . . He's come at the wrong time.

RINGIS *ironically* : Joséphine? *Sceptically.* Where are you going to get with all that?

>MARECHAL *follows him as far as the door.*

MARECHAL : All right. She'll wait. At your service, Captain!

>*They go out together. Camera stays for the moment on the door. There is noise from the room and the record of 'Frou-Frou' finishes playing. Pan back to the bar covered with the squadron flags. Camera holds and closes on the large sign on the bar, which has three drawings on it: a hunter, a crocodile, and a skull sketched round the following text: SQUADRON M F 902 — ALCOHOL KILLS — ALCOHOL DRIVES PEOPLE MAD — THE SQUADRON LEADER DRINKS IT. Captain* RINGIS, *followed by* MARECHAL, *comes in through the open door of his office. Camera tracks back and pans to the 'fellow from the General Staff.' This man wears a monocle and seems very haughty. He is waiting for them and examining the enlargement of an aerial photograph. He readjusts his monocle to have a better look . . . when* RINGIS *and* MARECHAL *come into shot.* MARECHAL *gives a military salute.*

RINGIS *to* MARECHAL : Captain de Bœldieu, of the Divisional Staff.

MARECHAL *saluting* : Maréchal.

BŒLDIEU *icily shaking the photograph* : I say, Monsieur Maréchal, do you know this photograph?

>*He holds it out to* MARECHAL, *who looks at it.*

MARECHAL : Oh, yes, Captain . . . Ricord took it when he

was with me.

BŒLDIEU: And is this Monsieur Ricord around?

MARECHAL: He's on leave.

BŒLDIEU: Of course!

> BŒLDIEU *goes over to* MARECHAL *and points at the photograph. Behind them, Captain* RINGIS *stands on tip-toe to look at the document.*

BŒLDIEU: It's that grey spot which worries me. . . . There, below the road.

RINGIS *interrupting*: It's not a road, it's a canal.

MARECHAL: Is it? I thought it was some railway lines.

BŒLDIEU *ironically*: What touching unanimity! . . . This precise detail gives one a fine idea of the perfection of our photographic equipment.

MARECHAL *shrugging*: Well . . . it was misty that day.

BŒLDIEU: I would like to resolve this enigma.

RINGIS: As you wish. . . . I'll ask for a fighter. *As he speaks, he turns to pick up the telephone.* Hello! Hello! Give me the pursuit squadron.

> MARECHAL *looks at the photograph again, then gives it to* BŒLDIEU, *and gets ready to leave.*

MARECHAL: I'll put on my stuff then, Captain.

> *He goes out. Camera stays on* RINGIS *and* BŒLDIEU.

RINGIS: What would you like to put on? A flying suit or a goatskin?

BŒLDIEU *still examining the photograph*: I have no preference. . . . Flying suits smell rather and goatskins shed hairs.

RINGIS *on the telephone again*: Yes. . . . Give me the pursuit squadron, please.

> *Through an open door of a German officers' mess, the German commander enters, followed by a few officers. Camera tracks back to show a part of the room, which is much the same as the officers' mess of Squadron M F 902. There is hardly any difference: a table set for a meal, a bar, bottles. The gramophone is playing a Viennese waltz by Strauss. But there are no drawings on the walls. Commander* VON RAUFFENSTEIN, *who has just come in, is still wearing his fighter-pilot's uniform. His back straight, his heels together, he takes a glass of*

15

spirits and downs it in one gulp, then he scratches his ear. (Still on page 2) He is small compared with the other officers surrounding him to congratulate him. His type is the Prussian squire: well-bred, strict, hard-faced. He speaks in German, as do the rest.

RAUFFENSTEIN *to his orderly*: Herr Bredow, take a car and go and look in the direction of the sugar plant. . . . I shot down a Caudron. . . . If they are officers, invite them to lunch.

BREDOW : Very good, Commander.

RAUFFENSTEIN *to one of his officers*: Herr Fressler, this is the moment to distinguish yourself. . . . You are going to concoct for us one of your famous fruit punches. . . . *Pause.* We ought to celebrate my second kill.

The other officers raise their glasses and surround him and toast his victory. RAUFFENSTEIN *drinks at one gulp, bending backwards to do so.*

FRESSLER : With pleasure, Commander. *He turns to the barman.* Give me three bottles of Moselle, two of Rhine wine, one of champagne, a half of Martel, one box of pineapple, three lemons . . . and sugar, of course.

During this list spoken partly off shot, pan along the bar to end on photographs of women pinned to the wall. Cut back to the door: BREDOW *comes in again and salutes. The music of the Strauss waltz is loud.*

BREDOW : There's two officers. . . . One of them's got a bullet in his arm; I've just taken him to the ambulance.

Shot of the whole room, taken slightly from above. After a time, BREDOW *enters again, followed by* BŒLDIEU, *then by* MARECHAL, *whose arm is in a sling.* BŒLDIEU *is always pretty immaculate.* MARECHAL *seems tired; he is wearing a jersey, his jacket is over his shoulders, his head is bare, his arm in a sling.* RAUFFENSTEIN *makes a sign to* BŒLDIEU *to come in and clicks his heels together. His officers do the same.* BŒLDIEU *gives them a dignified salute.*

RAUFFENSTEIN *in strongly-accented French*: Captain von Rauffenstein, Commander of Squadron 21. . . . We are very honoured to receive French guests. *Introducing his men.* My

16

officers. . . . Orderly. . . . Their coats.

BŒLDIEU *after saluting* : Captain de Bœldieu.

> *They shake hands.* RAUFFENSTEIN *turns towards* MARE-
> CHAL *and bows more formally. He is not very interested
> in this second Frenchman, immediately guessing that*
> MARECHAL *is not a career officer.*
>
> [*Long shot.* RAUFFENSTEIN *turns towards the barman.
> Hubbub.*

RAUFFENSTEIN : And your punch?

MULLER : May I serve you some?

RAUFFENSTEIN : Please do.]*

> *A German soldier removes* BŒLDIEU'S *overcoat while*
> RAUFFENSTEIN *leads everyone to the table.*

RAUFFENSTEIN *in French* : Gentlemen, please be seated.

> RAUFFENSTEIN *seats* BŒLDIEU *on his right and indicates
> the chair on his left to* MARECHAL. *Everybody sits down.
> In a medium close-up,* RAUFFENSTEIN *leans over to*
> BŒLDIEU *and speaks in French to him, putting on his
> monocle.*

RAUFFENSTEIN : I used to know a de Bœldieu. . . a Count de Bœldieu. . . .

BŒLDIEU *interested* : Ah, yes. . . . That was my cousin Edmond de Bœldieu, military attaché in Berlin. . . .

RAUFFENSTEIN *in English* : He was a marvellous rider. . . .

BŒLDIEU *in English* : Yes, in the good old days. . . .

> *Slow pan to* MARECHAL *and the* GERMAN OFFICER *sitting
> next to him.* MARECHAL *is looking at his plate.*

GERMAN OFFICER : Aren't you hungry? . . . You're not eating?

MARECHAL : Yes. . . . Yes . . . but . . . *He shows his arm in
the sling.* I can't cut the meat. . . .

GERMAN OFFICER : Allow me.

> *He takes* MARECHAL'S *knife and fork at once and cuts
> up his meat for him.*

MARECHAL : You speak French well.

GERMAN OFFICER : I once worked at Gnome, in Lyon.

---

*Square brackets denote a cut in the final version of the film for the
screen.*

MARECHAL *joyfully*: No joking! Me too, I'm a mechanic!...
*All heads turn in the direction of the door which they
have heard opening. Cut to a German soldier coming
into the room carrying a wreath. Camera tracks before
this imposing wreath in close-up to make visible the
words written in gilt on the ribbon around it: TO
CAPTAIN DE CRUSSOL, FRENCH AIR FORCE,
SHOT DOWN IN FLAMES ON MARCH 12TH
1914.... FROM THE OFFICERS OF THE GER-
MAN SQUADRON F S 21. Quick cut back to the
group shot at the moment when* RAUFFENSTEIN *rises
abruptly at the table.*

RAUFFENSTEIN *stiffly*: Gentlemen... *To* BŒLDIEU. I apolo-
gise for this... coincidence.

At a sign from RAUFFENSTEIN, *the music from the
gramophone is stopped. All the officers stand to attention in front of the table. Each bows his head. (Still on
page 2)*

RAUFFENSTEIN *after a moment of silence*: May the earth lie
lightly on our brave enemy. *All remain still.* Thank you,
gentlemen.

*Everybody sits down again. The Viennese waltz is re-
played on the gramophone and, while everyone is eating,
an old soldier appears at the door. He salutes, clicking
his heels together. He is a military policeman without
flashes, shown in medium close-up.*

POLICEMAN *in German*: Military police. I have come to take
the officer prisoners into custody.

*Dissolve on sound of clicking heels becoming sound of
train wheels.*

*Through the windows of a railway carriage, the country-
side is seen as the train passes. There is snow on the
ground; the sky is low and grey. Train sounds and
music. The original screenplay gave the following details: it is the start of captivity, seen through the windows of a railway carriage: the fields and the forests go
by. Winter landscape, frozen and mournful. Patches of
snow here and there. It is far away, very far away....
The train stops at last. Close on the railway sign:*

18

Very quick shot of a grey, drab, sad building, overlook-
ing a barracks yard. In the distance, a detachment of
some fifty hangdog Germans marches by in step.
Pan past the prisoners in the camp, who stand in a group
waiting for the convoy of new arrivals. Camera stays on
the still group of new prisoners, whose faces show an
extreme fatigue. There are French, English, Russian and
Belgian army officers. In the middle of this group,
BŒLDIEU and MARECHAL are brought out by the camera
tracking towards them. They stand side by side, the
first looking very haughty, the second tired and yawning
in a vulgar way. Seeing MARECHAL's 'incorrect' be-
haviour, BŒLDIEU looks at him with a certain contempt
from behind his monocle. . . . Resume long shot: a Ger-
man officer barks out a dry and brutal order, an unin-
telligible yell that makes everybody freeze. This German
is the Feldwebel KRANTZ. All the prisoners turn to look
at him curiously, as he produces a piece of paper. Before
he reads it, he gives the French officers in particular a
hard look. He reads slowly in French with a strong Ger-
man accent.

KRANTZ : In the name of Camp Commander Krauss, officers
will be treated with all due regard to their rank. Commander
Krauss, however, reminds you that you are subject here to
the authority of the German law. You will therefore, as of
to-day, learn German discipline and obey it.

Camera begins on KRANTZ at the start of his speech, then
pans along the German soldiers and the grave faces of
the prisoners.

KRANTZ *off* : Every German soldier working in a camp has
the right to give you orders and you will execute these without complaint. You will salute all officers according to German army regulations. In case of attempts at escape, the
sentries are ordered to shoot any officer discovered outside the

19

camp boundaries. *Pan continues past* Bœldieu's *quizzical look and* Marechal's *intrigued one.* It is strictly prohibited to dress in a slovenly manner, to congregate in groups, to speak loudly and disparagingly of the German nation, to quit your quarters after curfew, to communicate either verbally or in writing with civilians outside the camp. *Cut to* Krantz *who continues to read aloud from his text.* It is strictly prohibited to talk to the guards. *He folds up the paper he was reading and places it in his pocket; he continues in a jerky French, repeating the words by heart.* Now, gentlemen, we are going to make you proceed to an office for a small formality.

> *Long shot of the barracks yard. The guards make the prisoners march towards a building. Cut to a group of long-time prisoners who have been watching the scene.*

One of Them : Hey, new boys!

Another : Hey, look, tip 'em off!

> *They all begin to sing the tune of* 'Ange pur, ange radieux,' *improvising the words in chorus. In the group are certain characters who will be important later,* Rosenthal, The Engineer, *and* The Actor.

The Group : Ange pur, ange radieux. . . . Conceal your gold. . . . Hide your watches. . . .

The Actor *advancing* : Oh, yes, hide it well!

> *Immediately, the German guards jump on these disturbers of the peace and break up the group. Pan towards* Bœldieu *and* Marechal *who are queuing in front of a shed.*

Marechal : Hey, what are they getting at?

Bœldieu, *as though it were self-evident* : They are telling us to hide our gold.

> Krantz *intervenes and gets rid of the last of the singers. Camera stays on the group containing* Bœldieu *and* Marechal *as they get ready to enter the control shed. Medium close-up of a German soldier searching a struggling English officer rather roughly in the control shed.*

English Officer *in English* : Keep your hands away! Don't touch me! . . . Do you want my watch?

> *The officer takes his watch out of his pocket and throws*

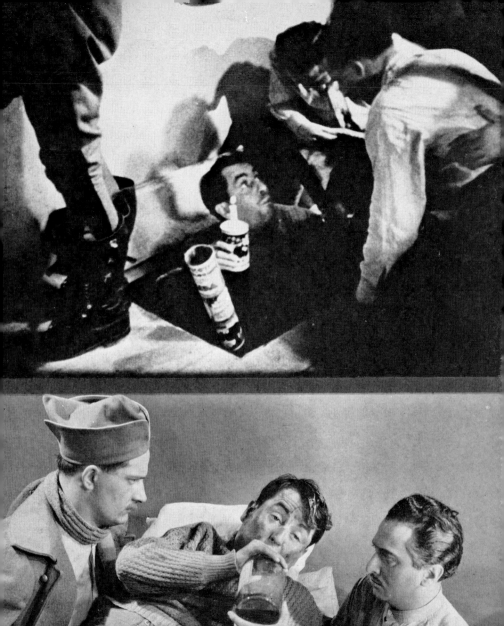

it onto the floor. Tilt quickly down to show the watch being smashed under the heel of the officer's boot. The German soldier bends over, and camera follows his gestures as he picks up the broken watch and puts it on a ledger where another soldier examines it and enters it in his book . . . during this, a hubbub of voices:

VARIOUS VOICES: Ah! Leave me alone! . . . Let me be! Those are mine! . . .

The German soldier motions over MARECHAL *who goes over, followed by* BŒLDIEU.

GERMAN SOLDIER: Look out!

He feels the arm of MARECHAL *that is in a sling, then rifles his clothes.*

MARECHAL: Sorry, mate. . . . Got nothing on me. . . . If I'd known I was coming here, I'd have brought along a little cash. . . . Sorry!

GERMAN SOLDIER: Nicht!

After searching MARECHAL, *the soldier turns to* BŒLDIEU *and gets ready to rifle the pockets of his fur coat.* BŒLDIEU, *very haughty with his monocle in his eye, stops the soldier and says in a glacial voice (Still on page 3):*

BŒLDIEU: But, I say, what sort of carry on is this?

The soldier finds a cigarette case, opens it, then lifts his head.

A GERMAN N.C.O. *in French*: I'm sorry, Captain, but it's our duty to search you. . . . That's war!

BŒLDIEU *very coldly*: I could not agree with you more, but there are polite ways of doing it. . . . Otherwise, I will be obliged to mention the matter to the Commander of the whole army corps.

In their room, the French prisoners surround one of their number, ROSENTHAL, *who is unpacking a large parcel that he has just received. A German guard watches it all carefully. Pan across the room in which several similar groups of men stand about.*

A GUARD: Open it!

Cut back to ROSENTHAL *who has not finished taking out tin after tin. Behind him,* THE ACTOR *taps him on the shoulder.*

THE ACTOR: How are ya, pal? . . . Keep smilin' . . . ya're happy!

ROSENTHAL *still unwrapping things*: Look, chocolate!

> *Off, an angry soldier begins to argue. Pan onto him: he is facing a sentry and he holds a wrapped tin.*

THE FRENCH SOLDIER: The bastards! You opened my tin of ham. . . . You haven't the right to! . . . No, you don't. . . . It's in the rule book. . . . And now it's gone bad!

> *Angrily and contemptuously, he throws the packet at the German, who does not budge. Cut back to* ROSENTHAL *as he finishes the unwrapping of his parcel.*

ROSENTHAL: Well, as for me, I'm always amazed and delighted every time I get a parcel from my parents. . . . When I think, here we are, in the middle of Germany, separated from our own kind by a line of fire we can't cross . . . and yet, here's a tin of peas for me straight from Paris!

THE TEACHER: What surprises me most is the incredible honesty of our gaolers.

CARTIER, *another prisoner*: Hey . . . that's true!

THE ACTOR *interrupting him in a Paris slang accent*: Our feldwebel, if he really is, Arthur, every day, he gets cabbage. He loathes it. . . . It sits on his stomach. . . . He told me so himself! I bet you he'd rather scoff your peas!

THE ENGINEER: Think it over for a second. If they had a go at our peas, people would stop sending us parcels. Then they'd have to feed us. They've already got enough trouble feeding themselves!

ROSENTHAL: Come. . . . Let's get a move on. Our guests must be hungry. . . .

> *Tilt slightly onto a table where three German N.C.O.'s are eating their lean rations. On a wall, a portrait of Kaiser William II. They speak in German.*

LEININGER: Ugh! It tastes like old galoshes.

ZINS: What do the Frenchmen get to eat?

ZACH: Cabbage . . . but they don't give a damn, they've got their tins!

ZINS: And the Russians?

ZACH: Cabbage roots . . . minus the tins.

> *They all laugh.*

ZINS : And the English?

ZACH : Plum pudding!

All three shrug and continue eating.

In the prisoners' room, MARECHAL *lights a cigarette with a bit of burning paper which* THE ACTOR *is holding out to him. They both smoke as they wait for* CAMILLE, *who serves as* ROSENTHAL'S *orderly, to finish setting the table.*

THE ACTOR *to* MARECHAL : In peacetime, I used to act at the Bouffes du Nord. Ever see my turn?

MARECHAL : Well, you know, I never go to the theatre. It's heavy stuff. Are you interested in the Tour de France? Well, I tell you, I've seen Chabert, then Petit-Breton, then those chaps. . . .

He goes on talking while camera pans around the room. Some of the men are moving towards the table. THE ENGINEER *goes over to* BŒLDIEU. *Near them,* ROSENTHAL *takes out food which he puts on the table.*

BŒLDIEU *a little surprised* : Are we allowed to buy everything we want, in town?

THE ENGINEER : Just about anything we want, through the canteen.

BŒLDIEU : Perfect. In that case, I will buy the English sort of arm-chair, some books, playing cards, English cigarettes. . . .

THE ENGINEER *interrupting him* : Oh, those. . . . You won't find that!

BŒLDIEU : No?

In the background, CAMILLE *hands a packet of cigarettes to* ROSENTHAL.

CAMILLE : Here they are, lieutenant . . . I'll try to come back tomorrow. *He salutes him in a friendly way.*

ROSENTHAL : Thanks, Camille. *He turns towards the two groups and waves them over to the table.* And now, my friends, if you'll be so kind, please be seated! *Hubbub; everybody sits down.* ROSENTHAL *continues, partly off shot.* Let me see, what will you have to start with? Cold chicken, paté de foie gras with truffles from Périgord or, Captain Cook's pickled mackerel?

The dinner sequence is made up of many shots of the various diners, taken slightly from above — only the more important shots are indicated.

BŒLDIEU *sitting down* : You keep a good table, as far as I can see!

MARECHAL : But don't we get fed here?

A NEIGHBOUR : In theory, yes. In practice, no. What they give us isn't eatable. Our parcels are enough ... *laughing* ... especially Rosenthal's.

ROSENTHAL : Come off it, it's nothing, really! *To his neighbour* BŒLDIEU. A little brandy, Captain, as an apéritif?

BŒLDIEU *haughtily* : Why not?

> *Quick dissolve to a few minutes later. Slight tilt onto* MARECHAL *and his neighbour at table,* THE TEACHER.

THE TEACHER : I've never had such a good meal in my life ... *holding out a plate to* MARECHAL ... Have a bit more fish.

MARECHAL : Yes, please.

THE TEACHER : And I'm beginning to get used to Rosenthal being so generous ... that just shows what adaptable creatures we are!

> *Pan to* THE ACTOR *sitting opposite* THE TEACHER; *he is listening and making funny faces. He has a cigarette in his mouth and brandishes a bottle. He makes broad jokes, always in his strong Parisian slang.*

THE ACTOR : Needless to say, the lieutenant is a teacher. ... Sister Ann ... anagram ... grand-daughter ... Waterloo ... *laughing at his own joke* ... Shit! That's a good one!

MARECHAL *ironically, beginning off* : You, you're quite a funny man, aren't you?

> THE ACTOR *stops laughing, as camera shows the whole table.* BŒLDIEU, *always stiff and unamused, leans towards* THE ACTOR.

BŒLDIEU : Do the rules of the game require that we pretend to find that funny? *He turns back to* ROSENTHAL. Congratulations, old boy, the brandy is quite up to scratch.

THE ENGINEER *taking the brandy* : Oh, it's the tip of the top, well worth it!

> *Cut back to* THE ACTOR *who surreptitiously picks up* BŒLDIEU'S *monocle from the table and tries to screw it*

in his eye and mimic Bœldieu *while* Rosenthal
answers.

Rosenthal *to* Bœldieu : It's the barman at Fouquet's who
sent it to me in a bottle for mouthwash.

The Teacher *not understanding* : Fouquet's?

Marechal *to* The Teacher : Yes . . . a bar on the Champs-
Elysées.

The Teacher : When I used to go to Paris, I'd eat my meals
at my brother-in-law's. . . . It's much cheaper than a restaurant.

Cut back to Bœldieu *and* Rosenthal.

Rosenthal *whispering to* Bœldieu : How long ago were
you last in Paris?

Bœldieu : A week.

Rosenthal : I envy you. Was everybody there?

Bœldieu : The other day, Maxim's was choc-a-bloc.

Cut back to Marechal *and* The Teacher.

Marechal *relaxed* : Oh, me . . . I never go to spots like that
. . . Fouquet's . . . Maxim's . . . I like a good cheap little
bistro better where there's a good line in wine. . . .

A Voice *off* : A bit of chicken?

The Teacher *in close-up, thoughtfully* : Maxim . . . I don't
know him either. . . .

Marechal : No loss to you, I can tell you.

The Actor *in a quick close-up* : We know! We know! We
all know you scoff at your brother-in-law's . . . *sings* . . . Frère
Jacques . . . Frère Jacques. . . . Dormez-vous? . . .

As he sings, he slaps Bœldieu *on the shoulder.* Bœldieu
*puts on his monocle and looks at him rather contempt-
uously.*
*French prisoners are walking about the camp yard. They
are seen from above through the glass of a window in
one of the camp buildings.* The Actor *goes by and turns
towards the window: with the fingers of his left hand
raised to his eye, he imitates seeing through a monocle.*
. . . In the courtyard, Rosenthal *meets him.*

The Actor : Hey, just a sec. . . .

Rosenthal : What is it?

The Actor : Is the . . . *continuing to imitate* Bœldieu

crudely . . . monocle around?

ROSENTHAL : No, I haven't seen him.

THE ACTOR : Because I just came from the canteen. You can tell him . . . his English-type chair . . . *gesticulates* . . . pie in the sky. . . .

ROSENTHAL *leaving* : All right, I'll tell him.

> *Camera tracks back from the window into medium shot of* MARECHAL *sitting among the baths and showers of the wash room. He still has his arm in a sling and* THE ENGINEER *is washing his feet. He looks out of the window.*

MARECHAL : Must say, he's nice, the chap with the tins . . . *pause* . . . He must be rolling in civvy street.

THE ENGINEER : I'll say. . . . You know the big bankers Rosenthal? MARECHAL *nods*. Well, mate, they're his mum and dad. Cross my throat, they really are.

> *As he rubs* MARECHAL'S *feet to dry them,* MARECHAL *shivers. (Still on page 4)*

MARECHAL : Hey, that tickles . . . *pause* . . . And what does he do?

THE ENGINEER : He owns a big dress designer's.

MARECHAL : That so? Funny. . . . If I had the cash, I wouldn't be in that line. What about you, what do you do outside this lot?

THE ENGINEER : Me, I'm an engineer for the ordnance survey.

MARECHAL *thinking* : Yes . . . on the ordnance survey.

> *Close-up of* THE ENGINEER, *then a series of shots of the two men as each speaks. Off, the sound of singing German soldiers.*

THE ENGINEER *getting up* : Eh, between you and me, your mate with the monocle, can we trust him?

> MARECHAL *is surprised by the question and* THE ENGINEER *looks as if there were a plot in the air.*

MARECHAL : Well . . . he's a bit lah-di-dah . . . but all the same, he's a good bloke ! Yes, you can trust him. . . .

THE ENGINEER *speaking softly:* All right, then. . . . *After a pause, he bends over to speak in* MARECHAL'S *ear in medium close-up.* Because, you know . . . at night . . . we dig a hole.

MARECHAL *surprised* : A hole? What for?

THE ENGINEER *as if it were obvious*: To escape!

MARECHAL: Impossible! But what do you dig your hole with?

THE ENGINEER: With the coal shovel and old tins. If my plans are right, we should come out at the other end in a garden, behind the buildings you can see over there . . . right out in open country.

MARECHAL: You can't get a move on with that.

THE ENGINEER: We've been working on it for two months. A few weeks more and we'll have it done.

MARECHAL *mocking*: Pooh. . . . The war'll be over by then.

THE ENGINEER: You think? You're under an illusion . . . besides, we like to get it ready just in case.

> *Camera tracks back as* THE ENGINEER *finishes wiping* MARECHAL'S *feet.*

MARECHAL, *both interested and sceptical*: And where are you digging this hole of yours?

THE ENGINEER: You'll see this evening, after roll-call.

MARECHAL: Thanks, mate, you've done me a favour.

digging a hole! Like Monte Cristo. I think that's very funny.

> THE ENGINEER *finishes his task and gets up.* MARECHAL *also jumps up.*

MARECHAL *wondering at the thought*: A hole? . . . So you're

THE ENGINEER: Come off it, it's only natural, with your arm.

> *Camera tracks forward into close-up on* MARECHAL.

MARECHAL: Look. . . . If you don't mind, I'd like to ask you something.

THE ENGINEER *off*: Go on.

MARECHAL: In fact . . . what's it mean, the ordnance survey?

> *After dinner. Before lights out, the German N.C.O.* ZACH *goes by calling the roll. Medium shot of him, in front of the door of the prisoners' room. He reads off the list he holds in his hand.*

ZACH: Maréchal?

MARECHAL *off*: Present.

ZACH: Bœldieu?

BŒLDIEU *off*: You ought to say, Captain de Bœldieu.

ZACH: Rosenthal?

ROSENTHAL *off*: Hmmm. . . .

31

ZACH : Rémy?

THE ACTOR *off* : Here . . . we go round the mulberry bush!

ALL *off* : Good night, Arthur.

> ZACH *has folded up the list of prisoners. He scans the room one last time and goes out, closing the door behind him. Quick pan onto the prisoners who get up quickly from their beds and listen to the sound of* ZACH'S *footsteps growing fainter. They all have solemn and wary looks on their faces. Each one gets ready in silence — this is obviously their routine every night at this hour — while* MARECHAL *on one side and* BŒLDIEU *on his bed look at them with surprise.* THE ACTOR *goes and barricades the door with a chair, then the others help him to screen the window with a blanket. (Still on page 4)*

THE ENGINEER : Whose turn is it?

THE ACTOR : It's mine.

> THE ENGINEER *and* THE TEACHER *go to a corner of the room. Tilt on them as they pull a bed aside and lift the floorboards, revealing a hole.*
>
> *Cut back to* THE ACTOR *as he gets ready. He ties a string round his wrist. Cut to the other end of the string tied round an old tin which somebody else is balancing on a shelf.*

MARECHAL *coming closer* : What's that?

> *As he speaks, he points to another empty tin which* THE ACTOR *is shoving into his pocket. On the side, there are more tins tied together.*

THE ACTOR : It's to get the earth out.

MARECHAL : And this string?

THE ACTOR : If I'm stifling, I pull it . . . and the tin falls over. It's the alarm signal. Then the lads pull me out by the feet . . . feet . . . feet . . . *sings* . . . marching up and down again! . . . *pause* . . . Right. Off I go. . . . To play the mole . . . ecule! *(Still on page 21)*

> *Pan to* BŒLDIEU *near* THE ENGINEER. BŒLDIEU *is holding some cards and seems to be playing patience.*

BŒLDIEU : Will it hold, your tunnel?

THE ENGINEER : It's got the right props, wood we've borrowed from the theatre.

BŒLDIEU : What do you do about the earth?

THE ENGINEER : We began by packing it under the floorboards, but now it's full up. You couldn't stick a pin in there. So now we put the earth in bags and take it for a walk with us.

Pan to THE ACTOR *who is ready for his job underground and slides on his belly into the tunnel. He soon vanishes completely, letting the string trail after him. A few seconds later, the string stops moving and lies loosely along the edge of the wall.*

Cut inside the hole where THE ACTOR *is face to face with his job. He sighs and attacks the earth.*

Cut back to the men leaning over the hole. They straighten up again, sighing. Still solemn, they smile as they silently remember THE ACTOR'S *bad jokes.*

Pan towards MARECHAL *who is acting as look-out. Suddenly he seems worried and makes a gesture as if he wants the others to be quiet.*

MARECHAL *in a very low voice, troubled* : Didn't you hear anything?

THE TEACHER *coming closer* : No.

MARECHAL : I heard something all right.

The others all listen and seem to indicate that MARECHAL *is dreaming.*

MARECHAL : I tell you, I did. . . . *pause* . . . There, there it is again. . . .

THE ENGINEER *intrigued* : We'll send somebody out to scout around. *To* THE TEACHER. Hey you, with that babyface of yours . . . you go and see what's up.

THE TEACHER : I'll say I'm going to the lavatory.

THE ENGINEER pushes THE TEACHER towards the door.

Cut to THE ACTOR *underground. He is digging and breathing with difficulty near his candle.*

It is night as THE TEACHER *nervously leaves the barracks and reaches the yard. He meets two German stretcher-bearers carrying a man and watches them in surprise, while the N.C.O.* ZACH *comes up to him on sentry duty with his gun at the ready.* THE TEACHER *pretends to be completely at ease.*

THE TEACHER : Arthur, I mean, what happened just now? ZACH : It's someone who tried to escape. We caught up with him in the gardens behind the buildings . . . so we shot him down.

THE TEACHER *worried* : Behind the buildings? Is he . . .dead? ZACH : I think so . . . *He begins to shout at* THE TEACHER . . . You, what are you doing out here?

THE TEACHER *looking stupid* : Me? I'm off to the lavatory.

> *He goes off.*
> *Cut to* THE ACTOR, *who drops his tool and begins to suffocate more and more and pulls the string.*
> *Close-up of the tin on the shelf. It falls onto a bed without a sound. Pan onto the group of prisoners at the window, anxiously waiting for* THE TEACHER *to come back. They are so absorbed they do not notice the fall of the tin for the alarm.*
> *Cut to the door as it opens.* THE TEACHER *comes in and the others rush over to him.*

THE ENGINEER : Well, what happened?

THE TEACHER *whispering* : Some one tried to escape. I don't know how. . . . They killed him . . . in the gardens . . . behind the buildings!

> *Dead silence. They are all very upset by the news. Suddenly,* THE TEACHER *starts; he has just noticed that the tin for the alarm has fallen on the bed.*

THE TEACHER : The alarm!

> *Camera shoots from above as they rush over to the hole and struggle to get* THE ACTOR *out.*
> *Cut to* MARECHAL *near them, embarrassed not to be able to help because of his arm. Cut back to all who are pulling on the rope. . . .* THE ACTOR'S *feet appear. He is pulled out of the hole and carried over to a bed, where he gasps for breath.*

THE TEACHER : Does it hurt?

> THE ACTOR *goes on gasping and shakes his head, while* ROSENTHAL *comes over with a bottle in his hand and puts it to* THE ACTOR'S *lips.*

ROSENTHAL : Drink some of this, old chap . . . drop of brandy!

34

THE TEACHER: It's the one from Fouquet's!

THE ACTOR *begins to stir on the bed as he feels better. He turns to* ROSENTHAL, *takes the bottle of brandy, has a swig, then sighs. (Still on page 21)*

THE ACTOR *singing*: I had a little drop about an hour ago. ... Don't break it!

He drinks some more. Pan to BŒLDIEU, THE ENGINEER *and* MARECHAL *standing; they sigh and look at each other with relief.*

BŒLDIEU: Whose turn is it tomorrow?

THE ENGINEER: Yours then, Captain, if you'd really care to!

BŒLDIEU: I'd be delighted. People have told me that crawling is simply marvellous as exercise.

Next morning. Mail is delivered at this time. Slight tilt up at the Feldwebel KRANTZ *guarding the yard. Behind him stands a German soldier.*

KRANTZ: I remind you that it is strictly forbidden to have clothes sent to you which are not military dress.

Cut to the yard. Many prisoners stand in groups, waiting for the mail to be delivered. Medium shot of a group made up from MARECHAL, BŒLDIEU, THE TEACHER *and* THE ENGINEER.

MARECHAL *to* ROSENTHAL: Anything new?

ROSENTHAL *without looking up*: A letter from my aunt in Bordeaux. She says there's an incredible crowd down there.

THE ENGINEER *leafing through the paper*: If I were them, I'd watch it. The Frankfurt Gazette announces a fantastic advance.

MARECHAL *sceptically*: Oh, right! They haven't even run up any flags. ... They're not ringing the bells. ... It can't be much!

BŒLDIEU *putting on his monocle*: Gentlemen, shall we proceed to more important matters?

THE OTHERS: Yes ... yes, of course!

ROSENTHAL: Yes, but not all at the same time.

They split up. A sideways tracking shot follows THE TEACHER *and* MARECHAL. ... THE ACTOR *catches up with them from behind, whistling between his teeth.*

THE TEACHER: I disapprove of this mania for exaggeration

in the German news items.

MARECHAL *gruffly*: Well . . . what about our papers? Remember, right at the start, how the Russian steam-roller was going to crush them?

> *Shock cut to* THE ACTOR *and* THE ENGINEER *reaching a corner of the yard set aside for gardening. They stop in front of a dug patch of earth, but a sudden sound of singing makes them turn their heads. Pan to what they see: a group of young German conscripts marching off to squad drill.*
>
> *Cut back to* THE ACTOR *and* THE ENGINEER, *as they hold a spade and a shovel and continue their previous conversation.*

THE ENGINEER: And what about famous General Winter, the one who was going to kill off all the bad Jerries with bronchitis and brace up the Allies?

THE ACTOR *bantering*: And what about Turpinite? Remember Turpinite? With a little bottle as . . . big . . . as a radish, we were going to kill off a whole army corps. They even tried it out on a flock of sheep!

> THE TEACHER *passes near them. As he walks, he shakes out the earth from under his greatcoat.*

THE TEACHER: Pity they didn't stop right there with the sheep!

> *While* THE ACTOR *watches out for the sentry who is standing beyond them with his back turned,* THE TEACHER *continues shaking the earth out of his coat, while* THE ENGINEER *conscientiously pats the fallen earth into place with his shovel. They sing a little tune. After* THE TEACHER *has finished, he walks off and his place is taken by the relaxed* MARECHAL, *who also begins to get rid of the earth in his clothing.*

MARECHAL *pretending to be interested*: Well then? What are you planting here?

THE ENGINEER *getting up*: Dandelions, my boy. Yes, I dream of making myself a dandelion salad with lard.

MARECHAL: Go on! . . . The war'll be over before your dandelions even poke their heads out.

> BŒLDIEU, *full of dignity, comes up to them. Cautiously,*

36

he takes a bag of earth from below his armpit and empties it. Then he folds up the bag meticulously, taking care not to get his gloves too dirty.

BŒLDIEU *haughtily*: If we go on with this odd business, we'll end up with hands like navvies.

As he finishes folding up his bag, ROSENTHAL *comes up and empties his bag, only more discreetly. Quick pan to a French prisoner, soldier* DRYANT, *who comes running up to them.*

DRYANT: Oy, Oy! Rosenthal! . . . The crates are here.

ROSENTHAL *delighted*: The costumes?

DRYANT: Yes . . . three crates, sent by your firm. We've taken them to the theatre.

ROSENTHAL *to the others*: Let's go there, boys. There must be one crate full of women's clothes . . . real ones! . . . *He leads the others off* . . . Are you coming, Captain?

THE ACTOR *is already on his way to the buildings: he hums and he walks waggling his hips and mincing crudely like a woman.* BŒLDIEU *does not move.*

BŒLDIEU: No thank you. My competence in theatrical matters is very slight indeed. Besides, I have something else to do. . . .

They all go off except for MARECHAL *and* BŒLDIEU *who remain standing face to face.*

MARECHAL *ironically*: A little game of patience, aren't I right?

BŒLDIEU: Exactly . . . I happen to be a realist. . . . *He takes the opposite direction, then turns round.* I'll see you later.

MARECHAL: See you later! *He laughs mockingly.*

Camera begins on English prisoners who are in a line on the stage of the entertainment hall, dancing and singing together 'Tipperary'. Camera tracks back slightly to show the whole rehearsal; everyone wears either a soldier's or an officer's uniform. Circular pan round the hall past the orchestra and past some groups busily making sets; pan ends on a German sentry who is keeping close watch on ROSENTHAL *and his friends, as he undoes the crates which have just arrived. These crates contain dresses, silk stockings, every sort of feminine finery. The sentry examines a corset.*

THE ACTOR *to the sentry* : Well, Arthur, found anything?

THE SENTRY *in a strong German accent* : No, I have found nothing.

The sentry takes a last look, about turns and goes off. Camera follows him to the door. [In the complete version, there is a cut to the sentry leaving the room and saying good-night in French. THE ACTOR wearing the hat of a marquis replies with the rest, but he says good-night in German with a strong Parisian accent.]

VOICES *off* : Good-bye. . . . Bye for now, Arthur!

Cut back to the group leaning avidly over the crates. ROSENTHAL waves an evening gown in the air and holds it on himself.

ROSENTHAL : Ah! These things have to be handled with kid gloves . . . and your eyes shut.

All are disturbed at the sight of this dress which they look at with great intensity.

MARECHAL : Real dresses. . . .

THE TEACHER : Look how short it is. Like a dress for a little girl.

MARECHAL *shrugging* : Eh, didn't you know? All the girls are wearing short dresses now . . . *looking at the dress again and sighing* . . . My! . . .

ROSENTHAL *ecstatically* : Just below the knee!

THE ACTOR : My old lady wrote and told me, but I didn't believe it.

MARECHAL : Hey, you! Put one on so we can see what it looks like. . . .

ROSENTHAL reacts strongly and stops THE ACTOR.

ROSENTHAL : No, not him. . . . He hasn't shaved properly. What about you, Maisonneuve, with your angel face? . . .

MAISONNEUVE : If you think that's funny. . . .

MAISONNEUVE goes off with the dress on his arm.

MARECHAL : It isn't only their dresses that are short. They've cut off their hair too!

Cut to concentrate on MARECHAL, THE ACTOR and THE TEACHER.

THE ACTOR *astounded* : You don't say. . . . It must be like

38

going to bed with a boy!

THE TEACHER: Really, when we aren't around to keep an eye on them, women go and do such foolish things. When I think of my wife, all these new-fangled things worry me. . . .

AN N.C.O., *an ageing professional soldier*: Well, I'm sure my wife hasn't had her hair cut off. . . . Bah, all that rot's only good for tarts!

They laugh while ROSENTHAL *takes some women's shoes out of the crate.*

THE ENGINEER: Oh, shit . . . shoes!

ROSENTHAL *happily*: We'd forgotten how small they were.

ROSENTHAL goes on digging into the crate and pulls out some stockings.

THE ENGINEER *overcome*: Stockings!

THE ACTOR *simultaneously*: Hey . . . stockings! Stockings!

THE TEACHER, *taking a stocking*: Silk! I've never felt silk like that before. . . .

Quick cut to another soldier gaping at a pair of black stockings. Slight pan to the soldier MAISONNEUVE *who appears dressed as a woman — skirt and top — and also wearing a wig. All the men turn to look at him and fall silent, curiously disturbed. How many memories and hopes are there. . . .* MAISONNEUVE *feels uneasy to see their intense looks on him. (Still on page 22)*

MARECHAL, *with forced laughter*: Don't you think it's funny?

MAISONNEUVE: Funny?

ROSENTHAL: Yes, it's funny. . . .

MARECHAL, *very sane and a little sad*: It's really funny. . . . You look like a real girl.

They fall into a heavy silence again. . . . They cannot find anything to say as they look at this soldier in a woman's dress. Very slow pan across the soldier's faces staring at MAISONNEUVE *in absolute silence. Pan ends on the transvestite who has come forward to the middle of the hall and who cannot help making a few feminine gestures.*

VOICES *off*: Yes. . . . It's funny!

The barracks entrance. The main gate opens and a large cart comes out, pulled by two horses and driven by a

39

German soldier. The cart seems loaded with crudely-made coffins. As it goes by, camera stays on the civilians who have followed the cart up to this point. Cut to two old grandmothers dressed in black, seen slightly from below in medium close-up. One of the old women sighs, then speaks in German.

OLD WOMAN : Poor lads !

Cut to the young recruits drilling in the yard. Orders in German are heard off : Attention ! Eyes front ! At ease ! *The recruits run off in step.*

In an annex of the entertainment hall, which ROSEN-THAL *and his friends have converted into a sewing work-shop, they are cutting out pieces of cloth and dresses to make stage costumes for the performance. Camera tilts onto the table where they are cutting and sewing. In the background,* MARECHAL *is seen standing near the window, not participating in these feverish and feminine activities. At the window,* BŒLDIEU *stands and looks out. (Still on page 22) Cut to a close-up of his expression of interest in the scene outside—the young recruits at drill. Cut back to the group shot, then cut back again to the close-up of* BŒLDIEU, *as he looks out of the window, turns to* THE ACTOR *who is singing and the others sewing, and then turns back to the window with the words:*

BŒLDIEU : On one side, children playing at soldiers. On the other, soldiers playing at children. [It doesn't really round things off !]

THE TEACHER *still sewing* : I'd like to know what's going on back home.

THE ENGINEER : Still no news?

THE TEACHER *mournfully* : Nothing.

THE ACTOR *cheerfully* : I couldn't care less what my old lady's up to. . . . What makes me want to slope off is, it's such a bloody bore. Ah, the Trocadero ! . . . Cadet Rousselle, and la . . . la . . . la . . . *he hums.* . . .

ROSENTHAL *interrupting* : In other words, you want to escape for the fun of it. . . .

THE ACTOR *with silly pleasure* : That's it !

THE ENGINEER *in close-up:* With me, it's just being contrary.

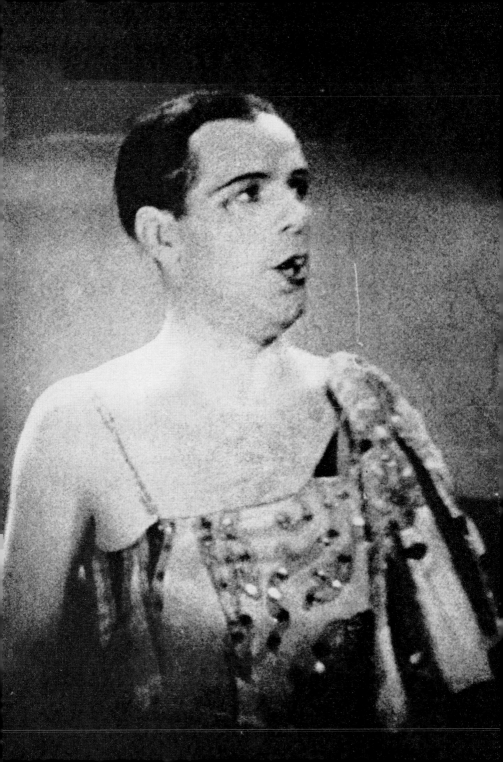

Ever since they've stopped me fighting, I've been dying to get back and fight.

Pan towards Bœldieu *and* Marechal, *seen in medium shot.*

Marechal *as though talking to himself*: I just want to do like everyone else . . . *more loudly*. . . . Besides, it gets me down to be here while the others are all getting knocked off!

Bœldieu *turning to him*: As far as I'm concerned, the question does not come up. *Medium close-up of him*. What is the purpose of a golf course? To play golf. A tennis court? To play tennis. Well, a prison camp is there to escape from. . . . What do you think, Rosenthal? You're a sportsman.

[Rosenthal: I want to escape so I can go on fighting for my country.]

The Actor: [Your country?] He's no sportsman! Why, he was born in Jerusalem!

In the medium shot of the group, The Actor *stands between* Bœldieu *and* Rosenthal, *who sits in the foreground with his back to both of them, facing camera with his head apparently lowered over his work. He looks down in the mouth, then he unenthusiastically puts on the panache of* Bœldieu *to answer back rather timidly.*

Rosenthal: Excuse me, I was born in Vienna, capital of Austria. My mother was Danish, my father Polish, both naturalized citizens of France.

Marechal *in a new shot*: Old Breton lords and ladies, eh?

Rosenthal *in a new shot*: Perhaps! . . . *still not looking at them* . . . But the rest of you, Frenchmen from way back, you don't own a hundred square metres of your country. Well, the Rosenthals in thirty-five years have found how to get hold of three historic castles with shoots, lakes, fields, orchards, rabbit warrens, fishing rights, pheasants, stud farms . . . and three picture galleries full of ancestors, every one guaranteed!

Rosenthal *has obviously reached the end of his tether; he turns on the rest of them.* If you think *that* isn't worth escaping for, to go and defend!

Bœldieu *looking surprised:* I must say, I had never thought of patriotism from that angle. How odd!

45

MARECHAL : Rabbit warrens! Fishing rights! Pheasants! Those flunkies of yours, I bet they scoff a lot of game.

Cut to a shot from above of THE TEACHER; *he has his pipe in his mouth and tries to follow the conversation. A hand pulls off the stage wig which he has been wearing.*

THE TEACHER *chewing his pipe* : I got into action a funny way. Believe it or not, I got into the army because I'm a vegetarian!

Cut to the surprised MARECHAL *and* BŒLDIEU.

MARECHAL : Vegetarian?

THE TEACHER *in close-up* : I'm not joking. My brother and I both had something wrong with our stomachs. So then the doctor told us . . . he told my parents first, of course : ' If you eat meat, you're done for.' *Hands put a clown's ruff round his neck.* Well, I became a vegetarian . . . and I got better. My brother went on eating meat . . . he became very ill. . . . He wasn't taken for the army.

While he finishes speaking, there is the sound of the boots of German soldiers, marching in step. BŒLDIEU *bows a little towards* THE TEACHER.

BŒLDIEU : I can see from your decorations . . . being a vegetarian has not stopped you from doing your duty.

THE TEACHER *nodding* : Nor did it stop my wife from sleeping with somebody else!

Suddenly a military band starts up: fifes, big drums, trombones. The heavy marching pace of the conscripts blends in with the sound of martial music. BŒLDIEU *goes back to the window, followed by all the others. Camera tracks back to frame them all as they watch the parade which is invisible.* THE ACTOR, *who is short, lifts himself onto the shoulders of* THE ENGINEER. *Pan in close-up from face to face during the following dialogue, as each watches the march past. (Still on page 23)*

THE ENGINEER : I must say, it's a good show!

BŒLDIEU *coldly* : I hate fifes.

THE TEACHER : Whatever they say, it really stirs you up!

MARECHAL *with the pan ending on his face* : What stirs you, mate, isn't the music . . . nor the instruments. . . . It's the noise. . . . [The sound of the march, just like in every army.]

The sound of marching grows louder. Dissolve to an-
other shot of the group. THE ACTOR, *still resting on* THE
ENGINEER'S *shoulders, turns and sees smoke in the room.*
Camera tracks in front of him as he dashes over to the
ironing board.

THE ACTOR: Blast! Burning. . . . *He picks up the hot iron*
from his trousers, which now have a hole in them. Furious, he
waves the iron in the air. With all your fancy chat and all,
my trousers are done for!

Cut to close-up of the ironing board marked by the hot
iron. THE ACTOR *lifts up the burned trousers to show*
them to everybody and begins to dance and sing.
Outside, the young German recruits are marching past.
Resume on THE ACTOR, *who walks backwards as he*
sings until he bumps into the door which opens. In comes
a sentry who takes a look round the room, then turns
towards THE ACTOR. *Seeing them all more or less dress-*
ed as women, and THE ACTOR *now humming to himself,*
he taps his forehead with his finger and leaves the room.
Night in the yard. Start on a close-up of a poster in
German and French, which has just been put up by a
feldwebel. In French, the headline reads:

Official Communiqué   General Headquarters
                                         20 February, 1916

DOUAUMONT IS CAPTURED

This is followed by a text that is hardly readable. All the
bells of the town nearby start pealing wildly.
Pan towards a lighted window and track forwards to
show German officers celebrating the victory in their
mess. They are drinking, singing, and playing the guitar.
One of them rises, singing gaily, and leaves the room.
Camera follows him: after a wave to the others, he closes
the door. As he walks in the cold night air, he goes on
singing, rubbing his hands together. Pan after him
briefly in the yard, then tilt up one of the walls of the
camp to stop on a window, where the French prisoners

47

*are staring in dismay at the joy and the celebrations.
Camera tracks towards them; the group includes* THE
ACTOR, BŒLDIEU, MARECHAL, THE ENGINEER, THE
TEACHER, *and* ROSENTHAL, *as they look down into the
yard. Suddenly,* THE ACTOR, *speaking gravely, breaks
the silence.*

THE ACTOR : With all that, are we still going to put on our
show?

MARÉCHAL : And how! More so now than ever! I'd even
suggest we invite, for once, the camp commandant and all
his officers, just to show them our morale's all right.

THE TEACHER : Things are going badly, if they've taken
Douaumont. . . .

MARÉCHAL *annoyed* : Who's saying no to that? All the more
reason not to cave in.

BŒLDIEU *turning to* MARÉCHAL : For once I agree with you,
Maréchal. I may not participate in your theatrical ventures,
but allow me to congratulate you all the same. . . . Good
show!

*Pan past German soldiers singing and toasting the vic-
tory in their canteen. One of them is playing the guitar
very loudly.*

*The wooden barracks hall has been turned into a theatre
for the show. Medium shot of* THE ACTOR *on stage. He
is wearing tails; the suit is a little too large for him, so
that the actual tails of the coat dangle too low. Even
though his costume does not fit, he sings and makes
gestures with great gusto. (Still on page 24)*

THE ACTOR *singing* : Si tu veux faire mon bonheur, Marguerite! . . . Marguerite! . . .

Camera stays on THE ACTOR *singing and moving about
on stage, as he takes the carnation from his buttonhole
sometimes to sniff it voluptuously, and as he tries to make
everybody join in the chorus. Then camera tracks back
on a crane to show the whole crowded hall. Prisoners
from all the camp are there. In the front row, satisfied
German officers. At the back, a few armed sentries
stand, as if at the back of a music hall.*

Cut back to a close-up of THE ACTOR, *singing and*

miming another verse of the song. A shot of him from the rear shows the audience laughing. Cut back to him as he makes the audience take up the refrain. [The original script added — In the hall, the men laugh and temporarily seem to forget their troubles and their imprisonment. THE ACTOR is pretty bad and the song he sings is vulgar. But he is so much a Parisian that all the Frenchmen are overcome by the number. As for the German officers, they stay rather stiff and scornful, hardly open to this little song from Paris.]

THE ACTOR *still singing*: Si tu veux faire mon bonheur, Marguerite, donne-moi ton coeur!

Everyone joins in the chorus now, even the Germans, caught up in the enthusiasm of the audience. All laugh out loud, except the German officers, who clap politely. Cut back to THE ACTOR on stage, as he wriggles with pleasure while he acknowledges the loud applause.

The curtain closes. Cut to the rudimentary orchestra, then cut back to the stage as the curtain rises again. THE ACTOR bows once more to a loud crash of music, then goes back-stage to lift a flap and usher in the 'girls'. These come on stage, dancing a sort of can-can. The 'girls' are five English prisoners, dressed in wigs, short dresses, jewels, and feathers. They dance and mince about in a poor imitation of women's airs and graces. They are a huge success! In comes the 'star', fanning himself with a lace fan and going up to the footlights to dance the finale to 'Tipperary' and then to a song like 'Frou-Frou'. (Still on page 24) Cut to a pan across the whole audience joining in the chorus, then back to THE ACTOR reappearing on stage, sitting on a cardboard motor-car, and also singing.

Cut to the wings, where ROSENTHAL opens a newspaper; he is very surprised, and makes a sign to MARECHAL and THE ENGINEER.

Cut back to the stage. Everyone is singing along with the 'girls'. All are having a good time . . . when MARECHAL, dressed normally, suddenly bursts onto the scene, pushing the 'girls' aside. He is overcome; he raises his

49

arms to get silence, the newspaper in his hand.

Marechal: Stop! Stop!

The orchestra stops playing. Everybody falls silent. Marechal yells in the total hush.

Marechal: We've recaptured Douaumont! . . . It's the boche news which says it!

For a few seconds, everybody in the audience is frozen. Then the orchestra strikes up 'The Marseillaise'. Everyone bursts into song and gets up at the same instant. The English 'girls' pull off their wigs and lead the anthem in French with strong English accents. (Still on page 41) Pan round the hall at all the prisoners singing in their emotion, while the German officers rise and leave hastily. Pan after the officers as they go out, then return to the men happily chanting in the hall.

Dissolve to a shot of German soldiers outside, as they run towards a building.

There is the sound of boots advancing in the dark; they seem to be walking down the steps that led to the detention cells.

Marechal is sitting on a prison bed, wrapped up in his army greatcoat. He is violently scratching away at the damp slimy wall with a spoon; the cell itself is dark and bare, having a bed, a blanket, and a door with a spyhole in it that lets in a sparse light. Pan towards the door as it opens. In comes the sentry Zach to investigate the noise that Marechal is making. Marechal turns wearily towards Zach and says nothing, but his face is angry. Zach stares at him, surprised and bewildered.

Zach *in German*: What are you doing there?

Marechal *stupidly*: There? A hole. . . . Yes, yes, yes! I'm digging a hole to escape: *He shouts the last word.*

Zach leans further forwards to look, and Marechal takes the opportunity to leap up, shove Zach onto the ground and run out of the door, which he slams behind him. Camera stays on the door, while the sound of struggling is heard on its far side.

Marechal *yelling off*: Keep your bloody hands off! Let me bloody be! Bloody . . . be!

The door opens again. Three soldiers carry in the half-conscious MARECHAL *and lay him out on the bed. Camera tracks in and tilts down on a close-up of* MARE-CHAL.
The shadow of a soldier falls on a poster freshly stuck to a wall in the yard. The poster reads:

DOUAUMONT RECAPTURED BY GERMAN TROOPS

German forces once again occupy the fortress of Douaumont after a battle which caused heavy losses to the enemy. We have taken 3,700 prisoners. The fortress is now safely in German hands.

Camera tracks backwards to show, from the rear, some French prisoners and German sentries or soldiers reading the poster which is in both the languages.

THE TEACHER : There can't be much of it left.

A PRISONER : Oh, you've seen it? It's terrible. Who'd have thought so?

A SENTRY *in German* : They don't say how many got killed taking it. . . .

In fact, the news by now hardly affects anyone. If the Germans take Douaumont or the French retake it, the war still goes on. . . .
Close-up from above of a mess-tin full of soup, then pan up to MARECHAL *still in his cell. He is sitting down, his back against the wall, dirty, unshaven, glassy-eyed. Sound of a key in the lock. He does not move. Pan to the door as it opens and admits an* OLD GERMAN SOLDIER, *who goes over to* MARECHAL. *A medium shot shows him looking at the untouched soup, shaking his head sadly, and slapping* MARECHAL *on the shoulder.*

THE OLD SOLDIER *in German* : Not feeling well today? Not hungry?

MARECHAL, *not understanding and shutting him up by shouting* : Stuff it, d'you hear?

THE OLD SOLDIER *moves away, but* MARECHAL *over-*

51

come by depression and rage, yells:

MARECHAL : I'm fed up, d'you hear. . . . Fed up! I want to see daylight, for god's sake! I want to see the light! Shit to this hole! I want to see the light, hear somebody speaking French . . . French, d'you get me, speaking French!

THE OLD SOLDIER, *feeling sorry for* MARECHAL *and sensing that the crisis is nearly over, sits down beside him. He would very much like to do something for the Frenchman. . . . He looks about in his pockets and takes out three cigarettes. Without speaking, he offers them to* MARECHAL *who refuses them. He puts the cigarettes down next to* MARECHAL *and goes on searching his own pockets, this time pulling out a mouth-organ to offer to* MARECHAL.

[MARECHAL : You want to make a bloody fool out of me?]

MARECHAL *turns towards the wall.* THE OLD SOLDIER, *very sorry for him, gets up and leaves behind the cigarettes and the mouth-organ. Camera follows* THE OLD SOLDIER *as he leaves the cell.*

THE OLD SOLDIER *triple-locks the door of the cell, then noiselessly lifts the hatch over the peep-hole in the door to look inside.*

MARECHAL *picks up the mouth-organ in the end, lifts it to his lips, plays it.*

Cut back to THE OLD SOLDIER. *He is satisfied and shuts up the peep-hole and walks down the corridor, humming ' Frou-Frou '. He meets a guard.*

THE GUARD *in German* : Why did he shout like that?

THE OLD SOLDIER *in German* : Because the war is lasting too long.

Medium shot of THE ENGINEER, THE TEACHER *and* THE ACTOR *who are smoking and talking softly together in their room.*

THE ENGINEER : If I calculated correctly, we'll be under the garden wall in four days' time. . . . Think of all those sacks of earth!

THE TEACHER : Now there's a chance of getting away and back to France, I'm worried about what's waiting for me back home.

THE ACTOR : Ah, there's more than one woman in the world.

THE TEACHER : There's only one for me.

THE ACTOR *as though stating the obvious* : That's why she sleeps around!

Pan towards the seated ROSENTHAL.

ROSENTHAL *sadly* : As for me, I can't bear to think we'll be leaving Maréchal behind.

Pan ends on BŒLDIEU *who is playing patience. He turns his head towards* ROSENTHAL, *takes out his monocle, and still keeps a card in his hand.*

BŒLDIEU : I too find it a bit depressing. It's really too bad, but that's war. . . . Feelings have nothing to do with it.

Quick pan to the door as it opens. MARECHAL *stands in the doorway with a soldier. He has just come out of the detention cell; he needs a shave, a wash, a comb; he is exhausted and dazzled by the daylight.* BŒLDIEU *dashes forward to greet him. Shot of the two men face to face.*

BŒLDIEU : Delighted to see you again, old chap.

All the others surround MARECHAL *to hold him up, for he is about to fall. They make him sit down.*

ROSENTHAL *fussing over* MARECHAL : Do you want to rest? Do you want something to drink?

MARECHAL *in a whisper* : I want to eat. . . . I want to eat. . . . I'm hungry.

Medium close-up of ROSENTHAL *hastily opening a tin and turning his head away to hide the fact that he is wiping a tear off his cheek.*

THE ACTOR *off* : Hey, come and sit here, [you'll be better off.] Rosenthal's getting some grub ready for you!

Dissolve to the same place, a few days later. The prisoners seem nervous and pace up and down the room. Clearly, tonight is the night they are going to try and escape through the tunnel which they have dug with such effort.

MARECHAL : What's the time?

ROSENTHAL : Eleven o'clock.

MARECHAL : Time's pretty fast today.

THE ACTOR *acting:* Yes, but this evening, auf wiedersehen!

THE ENGINEER : Rendez-vous in Amsterdam, then!

Medium close-up of THE TEACHER *and* THE ACTOR.

THE TEACHER: I've always wanted to visit Holland because of the tulips.

THE ACTOR: I prefer their cheese. Ah, Dutch cheese! . . . *Pause.* Don't you like Dutch cheese?

THE TEACHER: Yes, but tulips are pretty. They say there are whole fields of them, as far as the eye can see.

Pan to BŒLDIEU *playing patience.*

BŒLDIEU *turning to* THE TEACHER: Really, my dear fellow, you have the taste of a parlour-maid.

MARECHAL, *who is beside the door, sees* ZACH *enter. Shot first shows the two men, then the others clustering around.*

ZACH *in his strongly-accented French*: General roll-call at three o'clock. All officers are changing camps. Get your kits ready.

The prisoners stare at each other, dismayed, as ZACH *leaves the room, closing the door behind him.*

Pan across English officers grouped in one corner of the yard, then across ranks of French officers looking at them. Among the French are MARECHAL, THE ACTOR, THE ENGINEER, ROSENTHAL *and* BŒLDIEU. *They have just answered roll-call in the afternoon and are standing there with their kits, ready to leave.*

THE GERMAN OFFICER *in his strong accent*: Gentlemen, I wish you a pleasant journey and I hope you will see your wives again soon.

He salutes them, and the little squad of men begin to march away, waving to ZACH *as they pass by.*

THE ACTOR: Bye bye, Arthur!

GERMAN OFFICERS' VOICES *in poor English*: English officers, 'shun! . . . English officers!

BŒLDIEU: Perhaps we ought to warn them.

MARECHAL: What about?

THE ACTOR: 'Bout the tunnel, what else? That it's all ready for them.

When the two squads pass each other, ROSENTHAL *and* THE ACTOR *try to get closer to the English.*

THE GERMAN OFFICER *pushing them back*: Back to your ranks!

Cut to the English marching by. The suitcase of one of them springs open, its contents fall to the ground. Tilt down as the English officer bends, puts down his tennis racket, and begins putting back his things in his case.

Cut to MARECHAL *who profits from this little mix-up to worm his way to the English officer's side, as if to help him repack his case.*

MARECHAL *whispering in French* : Colonel. . . . Dans la chambre numéro sept.

THE ENGLISHMAN : It's really too kind of you. . . .

MARECHAL : Laisse-moi parler. . . . Il y a un trou creusé. . . . Préviens les copains.

THE ENGLISHMAN : I'm sorry, I don't understand French.

MARECHAL : Vous ne comprenez pas le français?

THE ENGLISHMAN : Thank you . . . thank you. . . .

MARECHAL, *annoyed and making signs*: Trou . . . un trou . . . dans le plancher. . . .

THE ENGLISHMAN *straightening up again* : Bon voyage !

A feldwebel comes up and puts an end to this conversation, roughly pushing MARECHAL *back to his squad.*

THE FELDWEBEL : Nicht aus der Reihe treten !

(The English and the French are allies in the war, but the English — who are going to be sleeping in the quarters vacated by the French — will never know about the tunnel beneath the floorboards.)

Through the window of a train compartment,* the flat, mournful, desolate countryside moves by. The train speeds through a station without stopping, then rolls on past more countryside. When the train seems to be slowing down, a large sign for a prison camp appears and stays on screen:

---

* *A still showing* BŒLDIEU *and* MARECHAL *sitting in a train compartment and guarded by the old soldier, who had the mouth-organ, suggests that Renoir did shoot some scenes inside the train, which were edited from the final version.*

KRIEGSGEFANGENEN   LAGER No 2
ALSHEIM
OFFIZIERSLAGER   C. K. V

*Dissolve to more shots of countryside seen from a moving
train for a few moments. Then the train slows again and
another sign appears and stays on screen:*

KRIEGSGEFANGENEN   LAGER No 9
SENTE
OFFIZIERSLAGER   C. K. XI

*Slow dissolve to yet more countryside seen from a moving
train. Finally the train begins to slow down, as the
officers move from camp to camp.*
*Night is falling. In the distance, a great fortress perches
like an eagle's nest on sheer slopes. The walls are in
massive grey stone, very thick; above them, a fortified
keep rises; above it, the imperial German flag.*
The train halts in front of yet another sign:

KRIEGSGEFANGENEN   LAGER No 14
WINTERSBORN
OFFIZIERSLAGER   B.G.K. III

*Camera starts on a huge wooden crucifix, then pans down
to its base to show an altar. On this altar is a framed
photograph of Kaiser William II. Pan in close-up round
the room to show the personal possessions of its occupant
— the camp commandant, who now lives in the old
chapel of the fortress. (He is* VON RAUFFENSTEIN, *who
shot down* MARECHAL *and* BŒLDIEU *and acted as their
host in the German officers' mess at the front. The archi-
tecture, stained-glass windows, and carved stone of this
curious room show its original purpose. The camp-bed
of the officer, his collection of riding crops and spurs, his
weapons, his valuable china and silverware look odd
in this room where the mass was once said. . . .* VON

RAUFFENSTEIN'S *plane has gone down in flames. He now wears a steel corset and moves with difficulty. He walks stiffly, like a puppet. He could have left the army, especially as he is an officer of the old school and despises the sort of work he now has to do; but he has stayed on for his country's sake. He continues to serve, mutilated as he is, in pain, the shadow of the man he was. . . .)*

Pan on past the commandant's belongings, including geraniums in a pot, a pair of binoculars and some daggers. There is a champagne bucket with a bottle in it, a leather-bound copy of 'Casanova' with a pistol lying on it, a framed portrait of a young woman, all resting on a small table. Pan ends on the commandant's orderly in the act of blowing into his master's white gloves to open up their fingers. They speak in German.

RAUFFENSTEIN *off*: Open the window. It stinks in here! Enough to make you throw up.

ORDERLY *standing to attention*: Yes, sir!

Camera tracks with the ORDERLY *as he goes over to the window, opens it to the sound of a bugle call, then returns to where he was.*

ORDERLY: May I bring it to your attention, sir, if you don't mind, sir, that we have only two pairs of white gloves left.

He shows the gloves in question.

RAUFFENSTEIN *off:* Too complicated to have some more come from Paris! Try to make those last out until the end of the war.

ORDERLY *standing at attention*: As you wish, sir. Would you require another cup of coffee, sir?

Tilt down in close-up on RAUFFENSTEIN'S *hand setting down a cup on the table where he is being served a large breakfast.*

RAUFFENSTEIN: If you must baptise this slop with the name of coffee. . . . I resign myself. . . . It'll warm my innards. *(Still on page 42)*

ORDERLY: As you wish, sir.

The ORDERLY *moves away, then returns, and, as he pours out another cup of coffee, he gives* RAUFFENSTEIN

57

a dossier. RAUFFENSTEIN *takes it and begins to read as he drinks his coffee. Front shot of* RAUFFENSTEIN, *putting his monocle in his eye to read. There is a knock at the door. Cut to outside the room where a German soldier is waiting in front of the door which opens.*

ORDERLY : What is it?

SOLDIER : The new ones are there!

Cut back to the room. The orderly leaves the door ajar and walks over to RAUFFENSTEIN.

ORDERLY *clicking his heels* : The new prisoners are in your office.

MARECHAL, BŒLDIEU, *and another French officer, Lieutenant* DEMOLDER, *are standing in the middle of the office. All three are looking at the half-open door. Pan with their gaze: through the doorway,* RAUFFENSTEIN *is seen as he gets up and sprays himself with scent, while his* ORDERLY *fusses over him and tidies his uniform. Finally,* RAUFFENSTEIN *picks up his sabre, his gloves and the dossier he has just been reading, then he walks into his office. He goes directly up to* BŒLDIEU *and bows and speaks in French:*

RAUFFENSTEIN : Delighted to see you again, Bœldieu.

BŒLDIEU *salutes, then shakes* RAUFFENSTEIN'S *hand as it is stretched towards him.*

RAUFFENSTEIN : I much regret seeing you again here.

BŒLDIEU : [We share your regrets.] So do we.

MARECHAL *muttering* : Yes, a bit!

RAUFFENSTEIN *glances at* MARECHAL, *then addresses all three men.*

RAUFFENSTEIN : Will you be seated?

MARECHAL : No thanks, sir.

RAUFFENSTEIN : At ease, then.

Very stiffly, RAUFFENSTEIN *walks over to his desk, sits down and opens the dossier. Tilt up on him as he reads aloud: there is a different shot of each man as he speaks.*

RAUFFENSTEIN : Captain de Bœldieu, four attempts at escape: via the heating-system, in a refuse cart, through a drain, and in a laundry basket.

BŒLDIEU *smiling* : There are times when one has to make

oneself rather tiny.

RAUFFENSTEIN *with a hint of a smile*: I quite understand. . . . *Returns to the dossier.* . . . Lieutenant Maréchal, five attempts at escape: disguised as a chimney-sweep. . . .

MARECHAL: You might say, sir, trying to win the sweep-stakes. . . .

RAUFFENSTEIN *continuing*: Disguised as a German soldier, disguised as a woman. . . . That is amusing! *His mouth twitches ironically.* Very amusing!

MARECHAL: Yes, but what was much less amusing, sir, was that an N.C.O. really took me for a woman . . . and I didn't fancy that at all!

RAUFFENSTEIN *ironically*: Really?

MARECHAL: Right! Absolutely right!

RAUFFENSTEIN: Lieutenant Demolder, three attempts. . . .

> RAUFFENSTEIN *gets up and walks in front of the three men as he speaks, smoking all the time.*

RAUFFENSTEIN: Gentlemen, your courage and patriotism earns my respect, but here the situation is something else. No one escapes from this fortress. You understand. . . .

> *The three officers nod.* RAUFFENSTEIN *sits down on the edge of his desk, facing them.*

RAUFFENSTEIN: So that no one can complain of German brutality, I have decided to use French rules and regulations here. . . . *He takes booklets from his desk, distributes them.* . . . Here is a copy of them. They will make good reading for you when you cannot go to sleep. And now, gentlemen, would you be so kind as to give me the pleasure of your company. . . . *He rises and calls his* ORDERLY. . . . Oswald!

ORDERLY *off*: Zu Befehl, Herr Major!

RAUFFENSTEIN: Mantel!

> *The* ORDERLY *hurries to pass* RAUFFENSTEIN *his cape, then his muff.* . . . *Dissolve to* RAUFFENSTEIN *as he comes into the fortress, followed by the three French officers whom he is showing around the place. The little group goes through courtyards and corridors, often patrolled by armed soldiers on guard. They even meet soldiers walking some guard-dogs on their leashes, as well as young conscripts at drill. There are various shots of them*

going up and down stairs until they finally reach an inner courtyard dominated by a watch-tower and mounted machine-guns. Some men present arms.

RAUFFENSTEIN : My men are not young, but they are amused when they play at soldiers. *(Still on page 43)*

Various commands in German are heard, off. The group goes down some steps, then halts in front of more soldiers standing at attention near machine-guns and field guns.

RAUFFENSTEIN *showing off the field guns* : I have twenty-five of those.

BŒLDIEU : Hm, really?

RAUFFENSTEIN : I suppose you know Maxims. . . . Excellent machine-guns.

MARECHAL *mimicking* BŒLDIEU : Why, of course, sir. Personally, I prefer the restaurant Maxim's. . . .

BŒLDIEU *tight-lipped* : Touché.

They all smile . . . then continue their tour. BŒLDIEU *and* RAUFFENSTEIN *walk side by side.*

RAUFFENSTEIN : I used to know a pretty gel at Maxim's . . . back in 1913. *In English.* . . . Her name was Fifi.

BŒLDIEU *also speaking English* : So did I.

They go by with MARECHAL *and* DEMOLDER *following.* DEMOLDER *stops* MARECHAL *to point out something. Quick pan to the wall to show a niche cut into the stone; it holds a small statue of the Virgin. Return on the two men.*

DEMOLDER *admiringly* : Twelfth century !

MARECHAL *shrugs. They go on until they catch up with the other two just as police dogs pass them again.*

MARECHAL *to* RAUFFENSTEIN : I beg your pardon, sir, but was this little home from home built just to put up me and Captain de Bœldieu?

RAUFFENSTEIN, *not understanding and adjusting his monocle* : Excuse me?

BŒLDIEU : Are we your only guests?

RAUFFENSTEIN *stretching out his hand* : Of course not ! Your comrades are behind there. . . .

Cut to a gigantic wall, then cut back to the group which

60

continues its visit, passing a statue set into the stone.

DEMOLDER *ecstatically* : Thirteenth century!

MARECHAL *bewildered* : Is that so?

But MARECHAL *does not give a damn for these details on the style of the prison. What he notices is the huge height of the fortress walls. Quick pan up this height.*

Cut back to the group which has reached the ramparts. RAUFFENSTEIN *leans over the edge of the precipice and shows the perpendicular fall of the walls down to the moat. Quick pan down.*

RAUFFENSTEIN : A drop of one hundred and seventeen feet. No one will escape from here.

The four men are back in the office after their guided tour. The prisoners are waiting to be taken to their quarters.

BŒLDIEU : It was very pleasant of you, sir, to have shown us around your estate.

MARECHAL *joining in ironically* : Yes, it's a really pretty castle, sir. . . . *Turning to* DEMOLDER. . . . So ancient! . . . *After a pause.* . . . And so cheery!

The door of the prisoners' quarters opens, showing RAUFFENSTEIN *and* BŒLDIEU.

BŒLDIEU *going in first* : I beg your pardon.

RAUFFENSTEIN *following him in* : I am sorry I could not have given you a room on your own.

BŒLDIEU : I am very grateful . . . but I could not have accepted in any case, sir.

MARECHAL *and* DEMOLDER *enter in their turn.*

RAUFFENSTEIN : Gentlemen, I hope that our little promenade did not overtire you?

MARECHAL : Not at all, sir . . . not at all.

RAUFFENSTEIN *bows, salutes and leaves the room by another door. Cut back to the three Frenchmen.*

MARECHAL *looking up* : Fourteenth century!

BŒLDIEU *unruffled* : Pure gothic!

At this moment, two German soldiers and an N.C.O. come over to search them.

N.C.O. : Do you mind? It's the search.

While the soldiers search the pockets of the Frenchmen,

the N.C.O. says to them with a smile:

N.C.O.: You know, your friend, Lieutenant Rosenthal . . . he's here.

MARECHAL *delighted* : I don't believe it! Old Rosenthal!

BŒLDIEU: I see his luck was no better than ours.

N.C.O.: The Commandant has given me orders to put you in the same room. . . . He says you'll be better fed that way.

They all laugh . . . but when one of the soldiers grabs MARECHAL'S *képi to turn it inside out and search it,* MARECHAL *loses his temper and snatches it back.*

MARECHAL: What's that? . . . Enough!

The courtyard of the fortress is covered with snow. DEMOLDER, *all bundled up, walks towards camera, reading something with great concentration. A sentry goes over to him and speaks to him in German, although inaudibly.* DEMOLDER *looks up and gives a friendly wave before he retraces his steps.*

DEMOLDER: Thank you, my friend. . . . Very kind of you.

In their new room, BŒLDIEU *and* MARECHAL *have indeed found* ROSENTHAL *again, as well provisioned and generous as ever, sharing everything with his fellow prisoners: a* LOCKSMITH, DEMOLDER *who is a professor of Greek, a* SENEGALESE NEGRO. . . . BŒLDIEU *spends most of his days playing patience. . . . The others read, work, smoke, chat, and feel bored.*

[THE LOCKSMITH *is telling the story of one of his ' amours'.*

THE LOCKSMITH: A good-looking blonde . . . big blue eyes. . . . An angel! Well, three days later I had to go and see the doctor. Don't trust a blonde!]

ROSENTHAL *is seated. Behind him,* THE SENEGALESE, *warmly dressed, is drawing carefully.*

ROSENTHAL: The same thing happened to me with a brunette.

MARECHAL: You can't trust anyone!

ROSENTHAL: She was a friend of my mother's! Ever so respectable. A real lady who did good works.

MARECHAL: It's usually clap which gets the posh people. . . . *Turning his head . . .* Isn't that so, Bœldieu?

66

Bœldieu : It used to be a question of class . . . as many other things were [believe you me]. But that, along with so much else, is becoming democratic. For the time being, the working class does not suffer from illnesses like gout or cancer . . . but it will some day, you wait and see. . . .

A group shot of the room shows Demolder *as he comes in.*

The Locksmith *to* Demolder : And the intellectuals?

Demolder : For us, it's usually tuberculosis!

Rosenthal *at the same time* : Here comes Pindar!

Marechal *getting up and walking around* : And the bourgeois?

Rosenthal : Liver complaints. . . . Intestinal. . . . They eat too much. . . . In other words, all the different classes would die of their various diseases if wars didn't come along to reconcile the microbes.

> Demolder *goes over to the table where* Bœldieu *is playing patience and begins to set out all the books he is studying. As he does this, he gets in the way of* Bœldieu's *game and displaces the cards with his dictionaries.*

Bœldieu *coldly* : Excuse me. . . . *He picks up two cards.* . . . Do you mind? Your dictionaries are going to be in my way.

Demolder *rather shyly* : I'm sorry, but it's such difficult work. . . . Pindar has always been so badly translated.

Bœldieu *eyeing him through his monocle* : Really? I'm sorry to hear it. Rotten shame!

Marechal *coming over to talk to* Demolder : I never asked you before because basically I couldn't care less, but who is this chap of yours, Pindar? *(Still on page 43)*

Demolder : You can make fun of it if you like, but to me it's the most important thing in the whole world. . . . No joking, I care about it more than about the war or even my own life. . . . Pindar is the greatest of the Greek poets!

Marechal : The greatest Greek poet? Well, I never!

> *Quick dissolve to a few days later, as* Marechal *goes off again to join* Rosenthal, *who is sitting on his bed consulting a large sheet of paper. The two friends, side by side, look at the map which* Rosenthal *has drawn.*

Rosenthal : Look. . . . *Pointing with his finger.* . . . We're here, above this curve, fifteen miles from the Mein. The only way to get to Switzerland without having to cross the Rhine is by Lake Constance. We'll have to walk two hundred miles.

MARECHAL : A nice little stroll.

ROSENTHAL : We'd have to walk for fifteen nights. We could hold out on six lumps of sugar and two biscuits a day.

MARECHAL : Really? *A pause.* . . . Want me to tell you something? You and your map, you're just as loony as him over there with his Pindar! *Nodding his head.* . . . Because, to get out of here. . . .

Behind them, THE SENEGALESE *rises to come and show them his drawing.*

THE SENEGALESE : There, I've finished. It's a picture of Justice hunting down Crime. I think it's pretty good.

MARECHAL *takes a vague look at the drawing, then begins to look at* ROSENTHAL'S *map again.*

MARECHAL : No, but, I say, to get to your Constance. . . .

Dissolve to a few days later, as MARECHAL'S *hands braid a rope in close-up. Pan to his face as he works.* ROSENTHAL *is by his side, examining the rope.*

ROSENTHAL : Do you think it's strong enough?

MARECHAL *pulling at the rope* : Oh, yes. It'll take the weight of ten like you and five like me.

Camera tracks back to show the whole room. THE SENE-GALESE *is posted by the door as a look-out. He suddenly turns round.*

THE SENEGALESE : Look out! They're going to search the rooms.

At once, everybody gets to work concealing everything that is compromising; MARECHAL *and* ROSENTHAL *dash over to a bed with their rope.*

MARECHAL : Under the mattress. . . . Yes. . . . Hurry up!

BŒLDIEU : Come, come, that's no good. It's infantile. . . . Allow me.

As BŒLDIEU *goes over to the window with the rope, cut to the stunned* MARECHAL *and* ROSENTHAL.

MARECHAL : Hey, well, I'd never have thought of that!

BŒLDIEU *dusting his fingers* : Out there the gutter's frightfully convenient.

MARECHAL : Look out! Here they come.

Each one goes to his bed. Pan towards the door. Five German soldiers enter. Pan down to MARECHAL *sitting on his mattress, reading a book aloud.*

MARECHAL : ' Louise wrote to Victor : I am as tired as a girl who has made love twenty-two nights running.'

As he reads, MARECHAL *has his belongings searched by a German soldier.* MARECHAL *turns his head towards the man.*

MARECHAL : Twenty-two nights running ! Think of that !

Pan to another German soldier searching THE LOCK-SMITH'S *pack. The Frenchman, who is stretched out on the bed, lifts his legs to make it easier for the searchers. Pan onto the table where* DEMOLDER *is absorbed in his work on Pindar. A German makes him rise and examines the stool beneath the scholar.*

Cut to the door as RAUFFENSTEIN *suddenly comes in, very dignified and smoking. He had not expected the prisoners to remain indifferent and seated. Quick shots of them all, intercut with medium close-ups of* RAUFFEN-STEIN *walking to the centre of the room. (Still on page 44) In medium shot,* BŒLDIEU *sits near his bed, while two German soldiers approach him to search his effects. He pays no attention to them and reads a book haughtily. Cut to* RAUFFENSTEIN *as he walks up to* BŒLDIEU.

RAUFFENSTEIN : Do not search that corner.

BŒLDIEU *gets up as* RAUFFENSTEIN *approaches, while the soldiers withdraw.*

RAUFFENSTEIN : Give me your word of honour that there is nothing inside the room which is against regulations.

BŒLDIEU *after a pause* : I give you my word of honour. Thank you. But why . . . *He moves closer to* RAUFFENSTEIN . . . my word of honour rather than any of the others'?

RAUFFENSTEIN *in close-up, ironical* : Hmm ! The word of a Rosenthal . . . or a Maréchal?

BŒLDIEU *in reverse close-up* : It is as good as ours.

RAUFFENSTEIN *in a shot with* BŒLDIEU : Perhaps.

They salute each other. Quick pan to DEMOLDER *struggling with a soldier who has grabbed his dictionary.*

DEMOLDER: No, not that one! No! No, it's for Pindar! Don't!

> RAUFFENSTEIN *goes over to the table and picks up the book which* DEMOLDER *is translating. He leafs through it, smiling. Then, with utter contempt, he throws it down on the table, examines with one hand* DEMOLDER'S *face, and shrugs condescendingly.*

RAUFFENSTEIN: Pindar. . . . Poor old Pindar!

> *He goes out, followed by the German soldiers. A few seconds later, the door opens to admit a prisoner from a nearby room.*

PRISONER: How did it go with you?

ROSENTHAL: Not too badly.

PRISONER: That's good.

> *The prisoner goes out. Pan to* BŒLDIEU *who is coming back from the window with the rope, which he puts on* MARECHAL'S *bed.* MARECHAL *immediately gets to work again.*
>
> BŒLDIEU *and* RAUFFENSTEIN, *standing in the commandant's office in front of the crucifix and the altar, are talking rather nostalgically about the days when they were not enemies. (Still on page 61)*

RAUFFENSTEIN: Any news of your cousin, Edmond de Bœldieu, the military attaché I used to know in Berlin?

BŒLDIEU *walking about*: Yes, he's doing very well. He's happy. He was wounded. He has one arm less and has married a very wealthy woman.

RAUFFENSTEIN: I am so sorry. . . . Such a good horseman!

> *While talking, they have gone over to the window and they sit down next to it. They suddenly talk in English.*

BŒLDIEU *seeing the miniature of a saddle*: Blue Minnie? Of course.

RAUFFENSTEIN: Do you remember?

BŒLDIEU: You were riding her when you won the Grand Military at Liverpool in 1909.

RAUFFENSTEIN: The Prince of Wales Cup!

> *They switch back to speaking French. Alternate shots of the two.*

RAUFFENSTEIN *after a pause*: Hmm! . . . De Bœldieu, I

would like to tell you something. Believe me, I feel nothing but distaste for my present job, as much as you do.

BŒLDIEU: You are hard on yourself.

RAUFFENSTEIN: I was a fighting man and, now, I am a bureaucrat, a policeman. It is the only way left for me to try and serve my country. . . . *He stresses the last word.* . . . Burned all over — that is why I wear these gloves. . . . My backbone fractured in two places, mended with silver plates. Silver strut in my chin, also a silver knee-cap. . . . I owe all this wealth to the misfortune of war.

BŒLDIEU: May I ask you something? Why do you make an exception for me by inviting me to your quarters?

RAUFFENSTEIN *in close-up*: Why? Because your name is Bœldieu, career officer in the French army, and my name is Rauffenstein, career officer in the imperial German army.

BŒLDIEU *in close-up*: But . . . all my friends are officers, too.

RAUFFENSTEIN *disdainfully*: You call Maréchal and Rosenthal . . . officers?

BŒLDIEU: They are very good soldiers.

RAUFFENSTEIN *with contempt*: Yes! . . . [Modern warfare, the nation in arms!] . . . The charming legacy of the French Revolution.

BŒLDIEU *smiling*: I am afraid we can do nothing to turn back the clock. *(Still on page 61)*

> RAUFFENSTEIN *rises and puts out his cigarette by the window.*

RAUFFENSTEIN: I do not know who is going to win this war, but I know one thing: the end of it, whatever it may be, will be the end of the Rauffensteins and the Bœldieus.

BŒLDIEU: But perhaps there is no more need for us.

RAUFFENSTEIN: And don't you find that is a pity?

BŒLDIEU: Perhaps!

> RAUFFENSTEIN *seems thoughtful as he looks at the window which opens on a sheer drop of one hundred and thirty feet. The pot of geraniums stands on the inner ledge, next to a small watering-can.*

BŒLDIEU: I do admire the way you look after your geranium.

RAUFFENSTEIN *turning back to him*: Do not think that I have turned into a botanist, but it's the only flower in the castle. . . . *He sits by* BŒLDIEU. . . . Ivy and nettles are the only plants growing here.

> MARECHAL *and* ROSENTHAL *sit side by side, smoking as they talk in the prisoners' room.*

MARECHAL : I'm glad to be escaping with you.

ROSENTHAL : With us both.

MARECHAL : Yes, of course. Mind you, I really like Bœldieu. He's a good bloke, but you can't let yourself go with him, you can't feel free. . . . A different sort of education. . . .

ROSENTHAL : He's a fine chap.

MARECHAL : I agree, but you see, if ever you and I found ourselves in a bad spot, we'd just be a couple of poor down-and-outs, but him, he'd always be Monsieur de Bœldieu. . . . *A pause.* . . . Besides, you're a fine chap, too! Look at how you've fed us with all those food parcels from your family !

ROSENTHAL : It was only from vanity. When I fed you, it was my way of showing you how rich my family is. . . . People think Jews are mean, but they're wrong. If anything, we're often generous, because we suffer from the sin of pride.

MARECHAL : That's all rot! What's the sin of pride got to do with it ! All I know is that you've been a good pal.

> *A new shot of the room shows a tall shambling man, dressed almost in rags, as he bursts in. It is a* RUSSIAN OFFICER, *also a prisoner. He speaks French with a strong accent.*

RUSSIAN OFFICER : Comrades! We have been sent a big crate. . . . A present from the Tsarina. . . . Do us the honour of coming to share it with us.

MARECHAL : A present from the Tsarina? That means caviar, at least.

> *In the great din rising in the room, the words, ' caviar ' and ' vodka ' are often heard.*
> *The Russian prisoners' room is in a distant part of the fortress. Everybody is over-excited, speaking at once and exulting over an enormous wooden crate stamped with the letter A. The officer who has invited the Frenchmen ushers in* BŒLDIEU, *who salutes, then* MARECHAL *and* ROSENTHAL *and* DEMOLDER. *They all shake hands and congratulate each other on their good luck.*

RUSSIAN OFFICER *cheerfully*: At last we may do something to thank you for your many kindnesses. The Tsarina . . . *He salutes . . .* has always been good-hearted.

Cut back to the crate which three soldiers are trying to open with hammers and various other tools. Everybody falls silent as the wood begins to give. Finally, the top of the crate comes off. Tilt down in close-up on feverish hands pulling off the top layer of straw. There is a lot of sawdust and straw, which means that the contents must be fragile.

VOICE *off*: Hurrah!

The Tsarina's gifts are finally revealed: the crate is full of books. The Russians speak in Russian.

A RUSSIAN *despairingly*: Books . . . books!

ANOTHER: What did you say?

ANOTHER: Books!

ANOTHER: Look underneath. . . . It isn't possible.

Medium close-up of the hands turning over the books.

A RUSSIAN: Nothing but moral treatises, grammars and Bibles!

Cut to MARECHAL *and* BŒLDIEU *and* ROSENTHAL, *who examines a book.*

ROSENTHAL: A *cook* book!

MARECHAL: Funny sort of grub!

BŒLDIEU *extremely haughtily*: Jolly poor joke.

A RUSSIAN: Let's set fire to it!

ANOTHER: Yes, fire! Burn the Tsarina's gift.

Quick shots of angry Russians round the crate tossing books and straw about, until the whole place is in chaos. As they do this, they mutter and curse the Tsarina and swear obscenely. DEMOLDER *tries to stop them from destroying the books.*

DEMOLDER: Stop! No, you don't have the right to burn books. For no reason at all!

The furious Russians, not understanding what DEMOLDER *is saying, shove him aside roughly and set fire to the crate. Cut to the Frenchmen.*

MARECHAL: Things are getting hot.

ROSENTHAL: We've got no place here.

73

ROSENTHAL *pushes his friends* BŒLDIEU *and* MARECHAL *towards the door. They leave just as German guards come running in to see what the racket is about. The guards try vainly to establish order, as flames begin to burst from the pile of straw and books.*
Cut to the three Frenchmen in the corridors, as more German sentries rush by to try to put out the fire and the revolt. Soon they are all alone, walking down deserted corridors as they reach the sentries' posts. There is noise in the distance. The three Frenchmen look at the empty walls with envy.

ROSENTHAL : All the sentries have left their posts! They've all gone to tame the Russians. . . . Look over there. . . . What a height, but nobody around!

MARECHAL *sighing* : If only we'd been ready, what a chance! We'd have thrown down the rope and in two secs. . . .

ROSENTHAL : Particularly as it's nearly night. . . .

BŒLDIEU : Well, we can try again another time. They've been good enough to organize a little rehearsal for us. . . . All we have to do would be to put them on a false scent. Now, we know that if one determined man got them to run after him, and if he could hold out for all of five minutes, his friends could escape during that time.

ROSENTHAL : That's a big risk.

BŒLDIEU : Oh, don't exaggerate. . . . *A pause.* . . . It would amuse me. When do you want to leave?

MARECHAL : Why us? You're coming too, old chap.

BŒLDIEU : No, Maréchal.

MARECHAL : Why not? Don't you think we can make it?

BŒLDIEU : Pfft! You know very well, that sort of thing wouldn't stop me going.

MARECHAL : Well, then?

BŒLDIEU : Your plan of escape can only work for two men, no more, and I know your preference as partners.

ROSENTHAL : That isn't fair.

BŒLDIEU : And what is fair in a war?

MARECHAL : Oh, no, no, no and no, old chap. [You'd be risking your life for us.] We can't accept.

BŒLDIEU : I am not asking your advice. I have made up my mind.

> BŒLDIEU *continues talking off, while there is a quick dissolve ending in a close-up of a squirrel in a cage in the prisoners' room.*

BŒLDIEU *continuing off* : I'm not against certain forms of entertainment. . . . In fact, I support them. . . . *A pause.* . . . Do you like music?

> *Camera tracks back to show* MARECHAL *seated on the left of the caged squirrel, playing with it through the bars with a straw. On the right of the cage,* BŒLDIEU *stands.*

MARECHAL : A bit, quite. A good waltz, yes.

BŒLDIEU : I'm extremely fond of the flute. We'll buy flutes for the whole camp and fix a date for a grand concert. This is the programme : at five o'clock, the full orchestra in all the rooms. That is when night falls. Five minutes later, our guards will confiscate the musical instruments. At quarter past five, there will be a new concert with all the instruments at our disposal — saucepans, animal calls, grinding teeth . . . and all you want. Result? We shall be summoned to a general roll-call.

MARECHAL : And then?

BŒLDIEU : Then? . . . *A pause, as he amuses himself with the squirrel.* . . . That is my affair. You will have five minutes to descend the walls and reach the woods.

MARECHAL : Listen, Bœldieu . . . I don't know how to say this. . . . For the first time in my life, I'm all embarrassed.

BŒLDIEU : Come, come!

MARECHAL : Yes, all embarrassed.

> *Dissolve to a few days later inside the room. Stay on* BŒLDIEU'S *corner of the room, which can be recognised by its neatness and the photographs of horses pinned on the wall.* BŒLDIEU *is by his bed, bending over a basin full of water and washing his white gloves.* MARECHAL *comes and stands in front of him, looking embarrassed and moved, not knowing how to begin.*

MARECHAL : Bœldieu, I'd like to tell you something.

BŒLDIEU *barely raising his eyes* : Could you pour out a little warm water so I can rinse my gloves?

MARECHAL *takes a pitcher of water and does what* BŒLDIEU *asks. (Still on page 62)*

MARECHAL : Listen, whatever happens, I'd like you to know all the same. . . .

BŒLDIEU *cutting him short* : But I'm not doing . . . I'm not doing anything for you personally. That excuses us from the danger of getting emotional. . . . *He laughs drily.*

MARECHAL : There are certain times in life, all the same. . . .

BŒLDIEU *quite abruptly* : Let's avoid them, if you please.

He has finished rinsing and squeezing out his gloves. He passes in front of MARECHAL *to go and hang them on a line.*

BŒLDIEU : May I?

MARECHAL *follows him and points at the gloves.*

MARECHAL : Are you going to be wearing that stuff?

BŒLDIEU : If you have no objection.

MARECHAL : No, but I must admit that it wouldn't occur to me to put on a pair of white gloves for this sort of job.

BŒLDIEU : Each to his own taste.

MARECHAL : You can't do anything like the rest of us do. I've been with you every day for eighteen months, and you still say *vous* to me . . .

BŒLDIEU *combing his hair* : I say *vous* to my mother and my wife.

MARECHAL : No . . . then. . . .

MARECHAL *admires* BŒLDIEU, *but he is disconcerted because he cannot understand him. He would like, just this once, to get closer to him, to bridge the gap.*

MARECHAL : I'd like to explain it to you.

BŒLDIEU *pretending not to understand* : A cigarette?

MARECHAL *sits on* BŒLDIEU's *bed.*

MARECHAL : English tobacco makes my throat itch. Everything really, your gloves, even your tobacco, comes between us.

These two men, who have faced the same ordeals equally bravely, will never be able to get along.

[*Fortunately,* ROSENTHAL *comes to put an end to their embarrassment.*

76

ROSENTHAL : I've warned everybody. First concert at five o'clock.

BŒLDIEU : Perfect.]

In a German mess, start on a close-up of an old ornate clock. The time is one minute to five. Pan to two seated German officers, as they smoke and speak in German. They are, in fact, promoted N.C.O.'s.

GERMAN OFFICER : You can say what you like, but wherever there's a German, there's order. Of course, I grant you the chief is a complete lunatic with his pot of flowers and all. . . . Lucky that I'm here. . . . I know how to keep that gang of devils in their place. Before I joined the army, I was a schoolmaster.

Night is about to fall on the fortress, perched like an eagle's nest on its summit. A flute concert strikes up in the distance. The two officers look up and go over to the window. The one who has not been talking bursts out laughing.

THE FIRST GERMAN *furious* : Lieutenant von Frittzwitz! Get those blasted flutes confiscated immediately!

In the corridors, a succession of quick shots shows the German guards running to the prisoners' rooms. The corridor outside the Frenchmen's room is empty. Suddenly, THE LOCKSMITH, then DEMOLDER and a few others come out of the room dancing and playing the flute. (Still on page 63) Finally, when they hear the sound of running boots, they go back into their room, still playing. Cut quickly to various rooms as German soldiers storm inside and brutally confiscate the flutes. In the room of the main characters, all are sitting around their big table, playing the flute for all they are worth. As soon as the German soldiers come in, they all stop at the same moment and raise their arms as one man to give up their flutes, which the German soldiers snatch away.

A SOLDIER *leaving* : I wouldn't start up again if I were you.

He goes out, slamming the door behind him.

MARECHAL : That's what we're going to do in fifteen minutes.

BŒLDIEU *takes another flute out of his pocket and looks*

at it with an ironical expression.

At one of the sentry posts, the German officer, who has been a schoolmaster, walks up and down, looking satisfied because the noise has stopped. He rubs his hands with pleasure. He turns his head as he hears a door open. Soldiers enter and deposit flutes on the table.

A SOLDIER *at attention* : Your orders carried out, Captain!

THE OFFICER : And now, parcels are not to be distributed until further orders. Only dry bread and water to be issued.

At these words, a deafening racket starts up, making the Germans jump. Dissolve on noise to the following shots: In a succession of different rooms, including the Russian one, the prisoners have picked up every object they can — saucepans, metal rods, forks, empty tin cans. All of them are doing their best to make as much noise as possible, while trying to keep time to the tune of ' Petit Navire ', a song they are all bellowing out at the top of their lungs.

Cut to various shots of soldiers, their arms at the ready, rushing down the corridors.

In the room of the Frenchmen, DEMOLDER is enthusiastically hitting the inside of a metal basin with a big spoon. The others also enjoy the din they are making.

Pan to ROSENTHAL who is winding the rope for escape round his waist. THE SENEGALESE is helping him do this. (Still on page 63) Pan continues round the room, showing MARECHAL also getting ready for the escape, and BŒLDIEU in his best uniform putting on his white gloves. Cut quickly from corridor to corridor. The Germans are trying to enforce order and push back the milling and shouting prisoners into the rooms.

Cut back to the Frenchmen's room. The door is shoved open by a German.

FELDWEBEL : General roll-call!

All the prisoners drop their noise-making bits and pieces to go out.

DEMOLDER : At last I understand my students. I never had so much fun in my life.

Last to leave is MARECHAL, followed by BŒLDIEU.

78

Camera tracks forward as Marechal *turns to the other man at the door.*

Marechal *very embarrassed* : Well. . . . *He does not know what to say.*

Bœldieu : What?

Marechal : See you soon.

With great dignity, Bœldieu *holds out his gloved hand.* Marechal *shakes it and goes out.* Bœldieu *closes the door and stays in the room. Then he comes towards the camera, does up his gloves, and takes the flute which he fastens to his lapel. He seems to be smiling as he does so.*

It is very dark in the courtyard of the fortress, and very cold. From above, all the prisoners are visible standing in rows under the searchlights and hemmed in by sentries. A certain disorder reigns, however, because of what has happened before. Many orders, given and cancelled, show that there is confusion among the Germans as well as the prisoners. Rauffenstein, *dressed in his long army greatcoat, enters the courtyard. Everybody stands to attention. (Still on page 64) A* Feldwebel *begins to call out the roll. Intercut from a close-up of him to shots of prisoners answering ' Present '. As he begins to call out the names of the French prisoners, pan across the faces of* The Locksmith, Demolder, The Senegalese, *and the others. All reply in turn, ' Present ', including* Marechal *and* Rosenthal.

Feldwebel : Bœldieu ! *No reply.* Bœldieu ! *No reply.* Bœldieu !

Cut to the nervous and surprised Rauffenstein, *shot from below. At that moment, in the dimly-lit courtyard, a single flute begins to play the tune of ' Petit Navire '. Everyone, startled by the thin and shrill sound of the flute, looks upwards. Pan up to locate this odd music coming from the sky, just as more searchlights come on and move their beams about in the darkness along the walls, prying into every hidden recess of the fortress. Everybody anxiously follows with his gaze the beams of the searchlights as they locate a flight of steps leading to the sentry posts at the top of the ramparts. A beam climbs up the steps one by one in search of the flute-player. Suddenly, a French uniform appears in the circle of the light. Slowly playing ' Il était un petit navire . . .' over and over again,* BŒLDIEU *is seen from below sitting on the watch-tower. The soldiers look up. Close-up from below of* RAUFFENSTEIN, *also looking upwards, trying to understand. (Still on page 81) Seen from his angle,* BŒLDIEU *climbs higher. (Still on page 81)*

Cut to a corridor inside the fortress near a window, where ROSENTHAL *unrolls the rope with the help of* MARECHAL. *They finally throw it out of the window, then* ROSENTHAL *lowers himself out while* MARECHAL *remains on the look-out.*

Cut to the exterior wall of the fortress, down which ROSENTHAL *is sliding on the rope.*

Cut back to the corridors. Soldiers approach. MARECHAL *closes the window and hides behind a column. The soldiers pass and, immediately afterwards,* MARECHAL *opens the window again and climbs out.*

Cut back to the exterior wall. The two Frenchmen slide down their rope, drop from the end of it to the ground and flee towards the woods.

In the courtyard, pan past the sentries all ready to fire by the searchlight. Everyone is looking up, watching BŒLDIEU'S *antics. He stops a few times to play* ' Petit Navire '. *(Still on page 82) Camera cuts quickly to him as he plays, then cuts back to the yard.*

AN OFFICER *in German* : If he passes the limits of the camp, fire at will !

Sound of rifles being cocked. Shot of BŒLDIEU, *still climbing. He has fastened his flute to his jacket so he can use both his hands to climb. Downward shot of the whole courtyard.*

A GERMAN OFFICER : Fire !

Various soldiers fire. BŒLDIEU *ducks and is not hit; he consults his watch, and goes on climbing higher. After the first volley,* RAUFFENSTEIN *stretches out his arm to halt the fire and walks to the centre of the courtyard to get a better view of* BŒLDIEU. *(Still on page 64)*

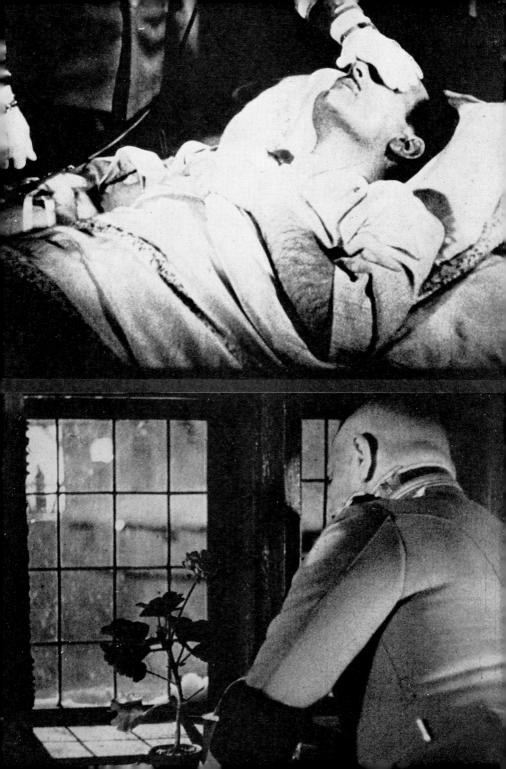

RAUFFENSTEIN *in medium close-up from above* : Bœldieu!
(Calling in English). Listen!

> *Cut back to* BŒLDIEU, *who straightens up and plays a
> few notes, then starts climbing again. There are a series
> of reverse angles.*

RAUFFENSTEIN *in English* : Bœldieu, have you really gone
insane?

BŒLDIEU *in English* : I am perfectly sane.

> RAUFFENSTEIN, *seen in medium close-up, is extremely
> upset; his voice trembles slightly.*

RAUFFENSTEIN *in English* : Bœldieu, you understand that if
you do not obey at once and come down, I shall have to
shoot. . . . *A pause, then he takes out his pistol.* . . . I dread
to do that. I beg you . . . man to man, come back.

> BŒLDIEU *has almost reached the ramparts and his voice
> seems to fall from the heights of the citadel.*

BŒLDIEU *in English* : It's damn nice of you, Rauffenstein,
but it's impossible.

> *From below,* RAUFFENSTEIN *is seen cocking his pistol,
> raising his arm, aiming and firing.*
>
> *Cut to* BŒLDIEU *who has been hit. As he falls, he takes
> a glance at his wrist-watch.*
>
> *Cut back to* RAUFFENSTEIN, *more still than ever. Very
> slowly, he puts his pistol back in his holster, then he
> walks about in the courtyard. After a time, a feldwebel
> goes up to him and comes to attention. Shot of the two
> speaking in German.*

FELDWEBEL : May I bring to your attention, sir, that Lieute-
nants Maréchal and Rosenthal have escaped.

RAUFFENSTEIN : Maréchal and Rosenthal! *He glances in the
direction of* BŒLDIEU'S *fallen body.* So that is why. . . .
Sternly. . . . Call out the dog patrols, alert the stations, and
the military and civilian authorities. Report to me about the
progress of the search every quarter of an hour. . . . That is
all.

> *Very slowly,* RAUFFENSTEIN *begins walking towards the
> camera.*
>
> *Close-up of a box containing the Extreme Unction, held
> by a military priest. Camera tracks backward to show*

BŒLDIEU, *who is lying in* RAUFFENSTEIN'S *room. The military priest, who has just given the wounded man the last sacraments, gets up and leaves on tip-toe, while a nurse takes up her place at* BŒLDIEU'S *bedside. BŒLDIEU is obviously being looked after with great care, and every effort is being made to nurse the French officer back to life. Pan towards the door where the military priest is going.* RAUFFENSTEIN *stands there in silence; he helps the priest to put on his cape and opens the door. As the priest leaves, a German officer comes up to* RAUFFENSTEIN *and they begin to talk very quietly in German.*

THE GERMAN OFFICER : Your orders have been carried out, sir. . . . The patrols have not yet located the escaped prisoners.

RAUFFENSTEIN : Thank you.

The officer leaves. RAUFFENSTEIN *closes the door. Pan with him as he goes over to the bed. The nurse moves away a little to give her place to* RAUFFENSTEIN. *He looks with obvious pain at the man he has fatally wounded, and sits next to the bed. Camera tracks forward to show both men in medium close-up.*

RAUFFENSTEIN : Forgive me.

BŒLDIEU : I would have done the same thing. French or German . . . duty is duty.

RAUFFENSTEIN : Are you in pain?

BŒLDIEU : I would not have believed that a bullet in the stomach could hurt so much.

RAUFFENSTEIN : I was aiming at your leg. . . .

BŒLDIEU : More than fifty yards away, very bad light. . . . And then I was running. . . .

RAUFFENSTEIN : Please, no excuses! I was very clumsy.

BŒLDIEU *speaking with difficulty* : Of us two, it isn't I who should complain the most. I, I'll be finished soon, but you . . . you haven't finished. . . .

RAUFFENSTEIN : Not finished dragging out a useless existence.

BŒLDIEU : For a man of the people, it's terrible to die in the war. For you and me, it was a good solution.

RAUFFENSTEIN : I have missed it.

THE NURSE *interrupting in German*: You are talking too much.

> *The two men fall silent. Close-up of* BŒLDIEU'S *face, strained with pain, gradually relaxing.*
>
> RAUFFENSTEIN *rises and goes to a corner of the room, opens a small closet, takes out a flask of spirits, and pours himself out a glass.*

THE NURSE *off*: Sir!

> RAUFFENSTEIN *freezes for an instant, downs his drink in one gulp by arching his back, then goes over to the bed.* THE NURSE *is unscrewing the plasma bottle; she looks at her watch and notes the time of* BŒLDIEU'S *death in her diary. Pan with* RAUFFENSTEIN'S *hand as he closes* BŒLDIEU'S *eye-lids gently. (Still on page 83) . . . After a while,* RAUFFENSTEIN *turns away and paces about the room, moving towards the window. He looks mournfully out of the window. It is snowing. Finally, he looks down at the pot of geraniums standing, as usual, on the sill. (Still on page 83) He looks at the only flower in the fortress for a time, then takes a pair of scissors and lops off the flower.*
>
> *Long shot of the countryside beneath the ice and the snow. Everything seems dead, the trees, the earth, the sky. . . . Not a sound, not a breath. In the background, coming towards us along a road, a wrapped-up human figure leads a horse. Slow pan over the countryside.*

ROSENTHAL *off*: God, he gave me a scare. . . . We ought not to have stayed so close to the road.

> *Pan continues down towards the voice. From above,* MARECHAL *and* ROSENTHAL *are seen, as they hide in a ditch near the road and wait for nightfall. Both men are dressed in shabby civilian clothes, dirty and worn out. They both wear felt hats.*

MARECHAL: So? We couldn't sleep in the rushes. They're full of water.

ROSENTHAL *sighing with relief*: He's gone.

MARECHAL *shrugging*: What, couldn't you see it was a woman? *He gets up.* Well, are you coming?

ROSENTHAL: Let's wait for night.

MARECHAL *is standing up, stamping and blowing on his fingers to warm himself.*

MARECHAL : Come off it, mate, I'm frozen solid. I've got to get a move on.

He moves off. ROSENTHAL *tries hard to stand up, but he has a swollen ankle. He finally gets up, slips, and painfully regains his balance again.* MARECHAL, *seen from below, advances towards the road. He turns his head towards* ROSENTHAL.

MARECHAL : Come on!

Cut back to ROSENTHAL, *looking pretty miserable as he finally manages to keep upright and reach* MARECHAL. *(Still on page 84) The two are seen slightly from below, as* MARECHAL *takes a tobacco-pouch from his pocket.*

MARECHAL : Do you want your sugar?

ROSENTHAL *takes his sugar lump and looks into the pouch.*

ROSENTHAL : Hey, there isn't much left.

MARECHAL *grumpily* : No . . . and we're not getting on much either!

ROSENTHAL *eating his sugar* : Don't you want some?

MARECHAL *closes the pouch and hands it to* ROSENTHAL.

MARECHAL : No, I had my share just now. . . . Here, I'd rather you took it. . . . Like that, I won't be tempted!

ROSENTHAL *looking at* MARECHAL'S *shabby coat* : Have you been eating your buttons?

MARECHAL : Can you see they're missing?

He shrugs and starts walking along the road which leads to a village; its church spire can be seen in the distance.

ROSENTHAL *hesitating* : Are we going on, then? Not waiting till night?

MARECHAL *pointing to the village* : Course not, come along. We'll go round the dump.

ROSENTHAL *walks on, limping. (Still on page 105)*

MARECHAL *further off* : What's wrong? Foot hurting?

ROSENTHAL *in pain* : No, it's nothing . . . just a sprain!

Dissolve to a new piece of countryside, less flat, but still covered with snow. Pan down from the top of a small hill to show from above the two Frenchmen sleep-

ing side by side, wrapped in their coats. Suddenly,
Marechal *wakes up and rises, shoving* Rosenthal
a little.

Marechal : Come along, off we go !

Rosenthal *gets up in his turn and follows* Marechal
*with difficulty. He walks very slowly, helping himself
with an ordinary stick which he uses as a crutch.*

Dissolve to a mountain road covered with snow. Marechal *is walking about five yards ahead of* Rosenthal,
*who is having more and more trouble keeping up. He no
longer even walks on his bad foot, but uses the stick to
hop along on his other leg.*

Marechal *annoyed* : Well, are you coming or not?

Rosenthal *furious* : I'm doing what I can.

They walk in silence for a time. Marechal *has slowed
down. They are side by side.*

Marechal *exploding* : You and your foot, you're getting on
my nerves !

Rosenthal *pathetic* : I slipped, it wasn't my fault ! *He
almost shouts.* I slipped !

*The two men stop walking. Pan to show them face to
face.*

Marechal : You slipped ! We know you slipped ! And when
we get pinched for lagging like this, are you going to explain
to them you slipped? Clumsy oaf ! We've got nothing else
left to eat, we might as well give ourselves up straightaway !

*As their tempers rise, the two men look at each other
with exhaustion and hatred.*

Rosenthal : Willingly, because I'm fed up, too. *He yells.*
Fed up ! Fed up ! Fed up ! If you only knew how I loathe
you !

Marechal : Believe me, it's mutual. Shall I tell you what
you're for me? A parcel ! Yes, a parcel, a ball and chain tied
to my leg. I never could stand Jews for a start, get it?

Rosenthal *trying to put on a brave show* : A bit late for you
to find that out. . . . *Waving his arms and yelling.* . . . Shove
off, will you? What are you waiting for? You're dying to get
me off your hands.

Marechal : You won't be able to say that twice. . . .

ROSENTHAL *all worked up*: Go on then, shove off! Shove off! Shove off . . . quick! I don't want to see your ugly mug any more.

MARECHAL *shrugging*: Right. Off I go. Try and get by on your own! See you soon.

ROSENTHAL: I'm glad . . . so glad. I could sing. . . .

MARECHAL *turns away and walks off more quickly than before, leaving behind the exhausted* ROSENTHAL. *Stay on* ROSENTHAL, *seen slightly from above; he works at his leg to try to make it better, but he is too far gone. He sinks onto a milestone by the roadside and stretches out his leg. His face is a mask of exhaustion, dirt and despair. His expression remains frozen for a time as he thinks of the awful end of this escape, so carefully prepared with his friend. It is not fair, it is horrible! Full of rage,* ROSENTHAL *begins to sing all by himself, just to show he still has something left in him — and so as not to cry. (Still on page 105)*

ROSENTHAL *singing*:   Il était un petit navire,
Il était un petit navire,
Qui n'avait ja, ja, jamais navigué,
Qui n'avait ja, ja, jamais navigué,
Ohé! Ohé! . . .

Cut to MARECHAL, *quite far away now, and walking with a determined stride. He gives a flick of the head when he hears* ROSENTHAL *begin to sing. Mechanically, he begins humming the song also as he walks. Camera tracks after him in medium close-up, as he sings and drowns out the more distant voice.*

MARECHAL: Au bout de cinq à six semaines,
Au bout de cinq à six semaines,
Les vivres vin, vin, vinrent à manquer,
Les vivres vin, vin, vinrent à manquer,
Ohé! Ohé! . . .

MARECHAL, *still walking, stops singing and can hardly hear* ROSENTHAL'S *voice, which still goes on singing stubbornly. Cut back to* ROSENTHAL, *who is yelling out*

*his song, his face increasingly distorted with sadness and
fury.*

ROSENTHAL *yelling* : On tira à la courte paille,
                On tira à la courte paille,
                Pour savoir qui, qui, qui serait mangé,
                Pour savoir qui, qui, qui serait mangé,
                Ohé ! Ohé ! . . .

Medium shot from above of ROSENTHAL *who suddenly
stops singing, listens carefully, and can no longer hear*
MARECHAL. *He is all alone now, abandoned. A pause.
Both morally and physically exhausted,* ROSENTHAL
*plunges his head in his hands and begins to sob; he does
not notice* MARECHAL'S *coat which is next to him in
shot.* MARECHAL *has, in fact, turned back and is looking
at his weeping companion. Camera tracks back to show
both men in medium shot.*

ROSENTHAL *finally becomes aware of* MARECHAL'S *presence and raises his head, looking like a whipped dog.*

[ROSENTHAL *almost pleading* : Why did you come back?
MARECHAL *does not reply.*]

MARECHAL *bends over and helps* ROSENTHAL *to raise
himself up.*

MARECHAL : Come on, mate ! Let's go.

Held up by MARECHAL, ROSENTHAL *walks a few steps.
New shot of the two men, walking along the road on
three legs with great difficulty.* MARECHAL *stops suddenly
and looks at his companion. All his hatred and annoy-
ance has gone from him.*

MARECHAL : You can't walk another step, can you?

ROSENTHAL *trying to be brave* : Oh, it's all right. I'm fine !

MARECHAL : Would you like us to stop at that little place over
there?

ROSENTHAL : You're mad . . . it's too dangerous !

MARECHAL *trying to convince himself* : It looks deserted. . . .
There's no smoke coming out.

ROSENTHAL : That's no reason.

MARECHAL : And when you're on a boat that's caught fire,
what d'you do? Chuck yourself into the water, don't you?

ROSENTHAL *crying and laughing with joy* : You're right. Let's chuck ourselves into the water!

[MARECHAL : Let's go then, chum!

And they start walking, step by slow step, towards a farmhouse.]

In a stable, MARECHAL *and* ROSENTHAL *sleep, hidden in the hay. Circular pan shows the stable's small stalls, a feeding trough, a ladder against a wall going up to the loft, an old cart. Suddenly, the sound of footsteps is heard outside. Cut back to a close-up of the two friends, who start up and begin whispering.*

MARECHAL : Did you hear? . . . Somebody. . . .

ROSENTHAL : You get out by the window. You'll have time to get away while they're dealing with me.

MARECHAL : Come off it! I'll handle this one! ROSENTHAL *begins to protest.* And keep still!

MARECHAL *rises. Stay for a few seconds on* ROSENTHAL *who cannot move. Cut to* MARECHAL, *who holds a thick log in his hands. He hides behind the door, waiting to knock out the first entrant. The stable door creaks, then opens to let in a cow. Behind the cow comes a young blonde woman. She looks so fragile that* MARECHAL *does not dare use his log, even though she can see him in the light of the lamp she is holding. When she sees the two men, she does not cry out, but remains quite still in her surprise. In a reverse angle, the men look so filthy and tired that pity comes into her gaze.*

She is young, dressed very decently in the style of all the local country women, yet slightly more elegantly and tastefully. Her face, framed by a kerchief, is delicate and beautiful. She looks gentle and rather sad. She shows no terror at seeing the two men and, as she closes the door behind her, she talks to them in German, as she knows no other language.

ELSA : What are you doing here? Prisoners of war? Do you speak German?

MARECHAL, *who has not understood a word, gathers all the same what the last phrase means.*

MARECHAL: No! *On the defensive.* No! Not bandits! French.

ELSA *in German* : French. Who?

92

ROSENTHAL *seen from above in medium close-up*: She's asking us who we are. *He shows his ankle, turns towards* ELSA *and speaks in broken German.* . . . I've sprained my ankle. . . . We're terribly tired. . . . We're not robbers.

ELSA : I'm not frightened.

ROSENTHAL *in German* : Call the police! I refuse to go another step. *He shouts in French.* It hurts too much. . . . No, I won't go another step.

ELSA : A sprain.

> *As she says this, she leans over* ROSENTHAL *and feels his ankle. Then she makes a decision and gets up.*

ELSA : Come into my house.

MARECHAL : What is she saying?

ROSENTHAL *to* MARECHAL: She's telling us to go to her house.

> *The two men hesitate and look at each other, not knowing what to do.* ROSENTHAL *is exhausted, but* MARECHAL *shakes his head.*

MARECHAL : I don't trust her.

ELSA : I live alone.

ROSENTHAL : She says she lives all by herself.

> ELSA, *carrying her lamp, leads the two men to the door of the farmhouse. They pause before entering.*

ELSA : Come in!

> MARECHAL *shrugs and aids* ROSENTHAL. *All three enter. Shot of the door from the inside. The kitchen is lighted.* ELSA *turns to the two men and says specifically to* ROSENTHAL, *who understands her language.*

ELSA : Don't make a noise, my child is asleep.

ROSENTHAL *translating* : She says there's a child sleeping. Don't make any noise.

> MARECHAL *helps her to seat* ROSENTHAL *carefully in an armchair next to the stove.* MARECHAL *remains standing, a little put out.*

ELSA *to* MARECHAL : Sit down, I'll be back at once.

> *She goes into the next room.* MARECHAL, *who has not understood, remains on the defensive. Shot of* ELSA, *putting down her coat and leaving the room. Cut to* ROSENTHAL, *comfortably seated, and to* MARECHAL, *standing and looking worried. Pan back to* ELSA *who is*

93

returning, carrying a basin. She goes and fills the basin
with water, and sets it down on the stove; then she puts
down a bandage and a towel next to ROSENTHAL. *While*
she waits for the water to heat up, she turns to
MARECHAL.

ELSA : Are you hungry?

MARECHAL *trying to understand* : Hmm. . . . Ah, yes!
Hungry ! . . . Yes. . . . Yes !

Cut to medium close-up of ROSENTHAL, *lying back in*
the armchair.

ROSENTHAL : She's asking you if you're hungry.

MARECHAL : Yes. . . . *Impatiently.* . . . I understood.

ELSA *to* ROSENTHAL : What about you?

ROSENTHAL *stretching* : I only want to sleep.

ELSA pours out some milk into a big glass held by
MARECHAL. *She then gives him a sandwich, which he*
begins gulping down. They all remain silent. After a
moment, the sound of a battalion walking along the road
can be heard. The soldiers are singing in the night.

MARECHAL *looks urgently at* ELSA, *then at* ROSENTHAL.
The sound of marching feet can be heard distinctly over
the singing. Suddenly, someone knocks on the shutters.
Cut often from MARECHAL, *alarmed, to* ROSENTHAL,
who gets up, to ELSA, *who calmly goes over to the win-*
dow, opens it, and pushes open the shutters. A young
feldwebel is standing at the window. Shot of ELSA *and*
the feldwebel talking in German.

FELDWEBEL : Good evening.

ELSA : Good evening.

FELDWEBEL *saluting with one finger* : Sorry to disturb you,
but how far is it to Wolfisheim?

ELSA : Seven and a half miles.

FELDWEBEL *sighing* : Seven and a half miles ! Well, I'd rather
be spending the night with you than on the bloody road to
Wolfisheim ! Still . . . *He salutes* . . . duty is duty. Thank you
and good night.

The feldwebel goes off. ELSA *closes the shutters and the*
window again with great simplicity, and she turns towards
the two Frenchmen, who are standing right by the door

94

and staring at her in bewilderment. MARECHAL *starts eating again, and* ROSENTHAL *sits down.* ELSA *goes over to the stove, picks up the basin and puts it down next to* ROSENTHAL'S *leg. She picks up his leg and begins pulling at his foot to get the shoe off.* ROSENTHAL *cries out with pain.* ELSA *is very sorry for him, but is also worried about the child. (Still on page 106)*

ELSA : Hush ! My child is asleep !

Very slow pan to MARECHAL. *He is watching the other two and understands their exchange.*

Close-up of a framed photograph of an N.C.O. Above the frame is the ribbon given for the top German decoration. The photograph is standing on the mantlepiece. It is daylight, and, as ELSA'S *voice speaks off, pan to show another photograph next to the first one: a group of young men.* ELSA'S *hand can be seen in shot, her finger pointing at various individuals.*

ELSA : My husband, killed at Verdun. My brothers, killed at Liège, Charleroi and Tannenberg. . . . *She sighs.* Our greatest victories ! . . . Now the table is too large. . . .

Pan to the table in the centre of the dining-room. ELSA'S *little girl,* LOTTE, *is finishing a slice of bread. She is five years old, brown-haired, blue-eyed, and looks very merry.*

MARECHAL *is looking after the cow; he is filling up her trough with hay. The fat cow, already used to him, comes to feed from his hand.*

MARECHAL : You're not scared, and you don't mind being fed by a Frenchman. . . . *Slapping the cow's side.* You were born in Wurtemberg and I was born in Paris; well, that doesn't stop us from being pals, does it? You're just a poor cow, and I'm just a poor soldier. And we're both doing our best, aren't we? Go on !

He pushes the cow aside and leaves the stable. Stay for a moment on the cow, which turns her head towards the door and moos.

His back to camera, MARECHAL *leaves the stable and goes over to take a look at the valley. He yawns and stretches luxuriously. The bells are ringing in the distance.*

95

After a while, MARECHAL *turns away and walks towards camera, humming. He goes off.*

MARECHAL *is now seen walking towards the farmhouse and, as he passes, he sinks his axe into the chopping block. He goes in.*

MARECHAL *closes the door behind him and walks over to the oven to sniff at what is cooking. In the background,* ROSENTHAL *sits in an armchair in the dining-room.* LOTTE, *the little girl, is next to him, and the two are chattering in German. From a new angle,* MARECHAL, *seen from the front, has stopped at the doorway which divides the two rooms. He is looking at* ROSENTHAL *and* LOTTE, *who have not yet seen him.* MARECHAL *himself has not seen* ELSA, *who was scrubbing the floor behind him.*

ROSENTHAL : You're a very clever little girl.

LOTTE *coquettishly* : Mummy and I know everything.

ROSENTHAL : Really? Well then, tell me how much milk the cow gives every month?

LOTTE : Mummy's the one who knows that. . . . *Counting on her fingers.* . . . What I know is I've got five fingers. One . . . two . . . three . . . four . . . five. . . .

Pan towards MARECHAL. ELSA, *behind him, tenderly gazes at her daughter. The young woman already seems to have got used to the presence of the two strangers.*

ELSA *in German to* MARECHAL : Could you go and fetch me some water, please?

MARECHAL *not understanding and turning to* ROSENTHAL: What is she saying?

ROSENTHAL : She's asking you to go and get some water from the pump.

MARECHAL : Well, of course. It's a pleasure. . . . *Turning to* ELSA. . . . Wasser . . . wasser. . . . Ya !

He and ELSA *smile at each other. He cannot speak a word of German nor she of French. They enjoy this game which makes it easy for them to be friendly.*

MARECHAL *takes an empty bucket and goes out. Stay for a moment on the door, with* ROSENTHAL *in the background, stretching in his armchair.* LOTTE *skips over to*

96

her mother, who is smiling at her, and throws herself in
ELSA'S *arms.*

It is Christmas eve. MARECHAL *and* ROSENTHAL *have put up a Christmas tree on the big table, shown in a long shot slightly from above. The tree consists of a big pine branch, which they are decorating with paper chains.* ROSENTHAL *is cutting out more pink paper, while* MARECHAL *fixes tiny candles onto the branches.*

At the foot of the tree on the table is a manger which they have constructed out of cardboard and wood. A quick close-up inside the manger shows a rather odd-looking holy family. The baby Jesus and his parents are carved out of potatoes.

MARECHAL *off*: It's sweet, but it still looks a bit shoddy.

ROSENTHAL: I did my best.

MARECHAL: Of course, you did. I was saying that to Father Christmas.

> ELSA *enters on tip-toe and looks moved at the surprise the two foreigners have prepared. It is obviously the very humbleness and oddity of it which touches her.*

ELSA *in German*: Oh! The Virgin Mary!

ROSENTHAL: And baby Jesus . . . *Smiling* . . . my blood brother!

> *He turns to* MARECHAL. *Shot of the three.*

MARECHAL: Touché, as poor Bœldieu would have said.

ROSENTHAL *suddenly sad as he remembers*: What, do you think he got knocked off?

MARECHAL: Better not to talk about it, all right? *He lights the candles on the Christmas tree.* It's ready. Shall we go and fetch Lotte? We ought to hurry, the candles won't last.

> MARECHAL *goes over to the bedroom with* ELSA. *Cut to* ROSENTHAL.

ROSENTHAL: Just a moment!

> *He goes over to the old-fashioned gramophone and winds it up. Cut back to* MARECHAL *and* ELSA *by the door, waiting and looking at each other tenderly. The lights go out.* ELSA *opens the door and goes up to her daughter's bed.* MARECHAL *remains in the foreground by the door, seen from the back.*

ELSA *waking up* LOTTE: Lotte! Hey, Lotte, Father Christmas has come!

> ELSA *picks up her daughter and carries her into the dining-room.* LOTTE'S *eyes begin to shine when she sees the tree and the lights. She slips out of her mother's arms and runs barefoot towards the tree and* ROSENTHAL, *who waits for her with open arms. Shot of* LOTTE'S *face above the table, looking ecstatically at the tree and the nativity scene. The faces of* ROSENTHAL, MARECHAL *and* ELSA *appear behind hers.*

LOTTE *overjoyed*: Is it for me? Oh! I want baby Jesus!

ELSA *leaning towards her daughter*: Do you want to take him to bed with you?

LOTTE: No, I want to eat him.

ELSA: He's not to be eaten.

> MARECHAL *smiles.* ROSENTHAL *is in the seventh heaven.*

LOTTE *reaching over to the manger*: I'll eat Joseph then.

ELSA: Eat Joseph, but in bed. *(Still on page 106)*

> LOTTE *turns to* ROSENTHAL *and kisses him.*

ROSENTHAL: You're a very nice little girl. . . .

> *He kisses the child again, very affectionately. Then* MARECHAL *catches* LOTTE *and picks her up to take her back to the bedroom.* ROSENTHAL *speaks to* MARECHAL *in German, pronouncing each syllable.*

ROSENTHAL: Lotte has blue eyes.

> MARECHAL *is silent for an instant. In the background, leaning against the bedroom door,* ELSA *seems to be lost in thought.* MARECHAL *repeats the phrase in German with a terrible accent.*

MARECHAL: Lotte — has — blue — eyes. . . .

> *A quick close-up of* ELSA *shows her smiling and correcting* MARECHAL'S *frightful German.*

ELSA: . . . Blue eyes.

MARECHAL: Blue — eyes. . . .

> ELSA *goes into the bedroom, followed by* MARECHAL *carrying* LOTTE *over to the little bed.*

ROSENTHAL *in the foreground at the door*: Goodnight, froglet!

> *Once the child is in bed,* MARECHAL *comes back and*

looks at the manger. ROSENTHAL *is next to him. They look at each other for a second, but say nothing and turn away as* ELSA *comes back after closing the bedroom door. Group shot of the three slightly from below.*

ELSA *embarrassed* : I . . . don't know how to thank you.

ROSENTHAL *answering in German* : Thank us? When we owe you everything!

All three remain silent for a moment. But the silence is too heavy, and ELSA *breaks it.*

ELSA *first to* ROSENTHAL : Well then, goodnight.

They shake hands affectionately and ROSENTHAL *gets ready to go to his room.*

MARECHAL *to* ROSENTHAL : Goodnight!

Pan to the gramophone which is still playing. MARECHAL *goes and turns it off.* ELSA *is still standing in the middle of the room, her eyes lowered.*

MARECHAL *to* ELSA : Goodnight.

ELSA *without raising her head and in French* : Goodnight.

MARECHAL *walks to the door of* ROSENTHAL'S *room, then returns before opening it. Casually, he goes over to the Christmas tree and blows out the lighted candles. He then walks off again. Stay on* ELSA *for a few seconds, then cut to* MARECHAL *who goes into* ROSENTHAL'S *room with the camera following him.* MARECHAL *whispers, 'Goodnight', and leaves by another door to go into his own room. He closes the door behind him.*

Medium close-up of MARECHAL, *looking thoughtful. When he has closed the door, he turns his head towards the dresser. On the dresser is a tray full of apples set out to dry. He takes one and begins eating it, as he walks about the room. Follow him to show at the same time as he notices it, that the door leading from his room to the dining-room is ajar. In the background,* ELSA *is still standing where he left her.* MARECHAL, *surprised, goes up to her very slowly until he is standing right next to her. She raises her face and he takes her in his arms.*

Cut to the snowy countryside seen by ROSENTHAL *from the window of his room. Camera tracks backward to show* ROSENTHAL, *seen from the back, leaning against*

the windowsill. He moves away.
ROSENTHAL *leaves the window. Follow him to the door which leads to the dining-room. He opens it and sees* MARECHAL *holding* ELSA *in his arms.*
Taken by surprise, MARECHAL *and* ELSA *move apart.* ROSENTHAL *goes over to* ELSA *and shakes her hand.*
ROSENTHAL : Hello . . . I'll do the coffee.
MARECHAL *a bit embarrassed* : We were waiting for you. . . . Coffee's ready. *He turns towards* ELSA *tenderly.* Tell him in French.
ELSA, *in close-up, shyly pronounces each syllable distinctly in French.*
ELSA : Coff . . . ee . . . is . . . read . . . ee. . . .
This insignificant little phrase is her declaration of love. . . . And all three look at each other, laughing. . . . But ROSENTHAL'S *ankle has already healed. The two men will have to leave soon. Quick dissolve to medium shot of the two men, seen from the back, leaning against the fence, which is the farm's boundary.*
ROSENTHAL : Have you warned her we're leaving?
MARECHAL *without turning round* : No, not yet.
ROSENTHAL : You must, you know. . . .
MARECHAL *embarrassed* : You go and tell her . . . [please . . . I can't bring myself to.]
ROSENTHAL, *extremely put out by the prospect, nonetheless goes off in the direction of the farm.* MARECHAL, *his back still turned, lowers his head a little.*
Medium shot of ELSA: *her expression shows that she is expecting the news. The door makes a noise as* ROSENTHAL, *looking downcast, comes in.*
ROSENTHAL *in German* : We'll be leaving this evening and . . . .
ELSA *interrupting him in German* : I knew it.
ROSENTHAL : Maréchal is so sad that he didn't dare tell you himself.
ELSA : Why? I always knew he would be leaving one of these days.
She rushes out of the room. ROSENTHAL *opens the window. In the background is* MARECHAL *leaning against*

the fence.

ROSENTHAL : Come in!

MARECHAL, *in the distance, straightens up and walks over to the farm house.*

MARECHAL : Yes. . . . Coming. . . .

ROSENTHAL, *in the foreground, closes the window.*

LOTTE *is eating by herself at the big table. Three other bowls are set on the table.* ELSA, *holding a coffee pot, comes into shot and pours out the coffee.* MARECHAL, *his head lowered, sits down, while* ROSENTHAL *goes over to the little girl and strokes her hair.* ELSA *speaks in German, showing some parcels with a gesture of her head.*

ELSA : Those parcels are for the. . . . You must eat something hot before you leave.

ROSENTHAL *to* MARECHAL : Well, we won't start till nightfall then?

Cut to ELSA *in medium close-up. She seems out of breath and sets down the coffee pot on the table to go quickly over into a corner. Follow her, as she sits down and starts weeping. Cut back to* MARECHAL, *who has immediately got up. He goes over to her. Medium close-up of the two, who remain silent for a moment.*

Cut back to the table. ROSENTHAL, *wanting to leave the lovers alone for the last time, begins to make discreetly for the door, then turns back to go and fetch* LOTTE, *whom he pulls towards the door.*

ROSENTHAL : Come along, Lotte. Let's go and say goodbye to the cow.

They go out. Cut back to the couple, still sitting on the bench next to the fireplace, holding hands. ELSA *speaks in German,* MARECHAL *in French. They speak at random, but they know that their words are words of love.*

ELSA : I was alone for such a long time. . . . I had stopped waiting. . . . You will never know the joy it gave me to hear your man's footsteps in this house. . . .

She begins to sob.

MARECHAL : Elsa, listen . . . when the war is over. . . . If I don't get killed, I'll come back. I'll take you and Lotte back

101

to France. . . .

Dissolve to a few hours later:
The moment of departure has come: the two friends
are wearing the same old clothes — now clean and
patched — and ROSENTHAL *has put* ELSA'S *small parcels*
in his pockets.

ELSA *stands very straight and dry-eyed.* LOTTE *is holding*
onto her skirt. ELSA *speaks to* MARECHAL.

ELSA *in German* : Go quickly. . . . It's better that way!

MARECHAL *presses her hand a long time; he would like*
to say something to soothe her, knowing how upset she
is; but what can he say that she will understand? Sud-
denly, he picks up LOTTE *and holds her in his arms. He*
speaks syllable by syllable in German with his execrable
accent.

MARECHAL : Lotte — has — blue — eyes.

MARECHAL *has put all his love, all his gratitude, and*
more still in this odd farewell. Quick cut to a close-up
of ELSA, *correcting him.*

ELSA : Lotte has blue eyes.

Overwhelmed, MARECHAL *leaves the room, followed by*
ROSENTHAL.
Cut to a night exterior. The two men go forward.
MARECHAL *hesitates to look back.*
Cut back to the room. ELSA *and* LOTTE *are standing at*
the open door, looking at the two friends walking away.
(Still on page 107) Cut to MARECHAL *who looks back.*
In the background is the lighted door and ELSA, *holding*
LOTTE *against her. At that moment:*

ROSENTHAL : Look back!

MARECHAL *pretends not to have looked back.*

MARECHAL *grumbling* : If I'd looked back, I might not be
able to leave. . . .

Cut back to ELSA *and* LOTTE *still at the door.* ELSA
makes up her mind, closes the door and takes her
daughter over to the table, putting her in front of a bowl.
She starts moving about busily, removing plates and
glasses, then leaves the room. Stay on the little girl.
Pan to reveal the mountains, covered with snow, then

show from above MARECHAL *and* ROSENTHAL *on the look out, in hiding behind some pine-trees. (Still on page 108) They have been walking for two nights and have reached the Swiss border. Their only problem now is to avoid German patrols guarding the frontier. So the two men have been hiding at the edge of a wood, as they examine the deserted landscape, all covered in snow.*

ROSENTHAL : Well, aren't we going to wait till night?

MARECHAL : Not a chance. We'd lose our way. Besides, the wood is so thick, when we get to the valley, we can go on our hands and knees. *A pause.* Are you sure, at least, that that's Switzerland over there?

ROSENTHAL *looking at his map* : Absolutely sure.

Quick pan over the valley and come back to the two men.

MARECHAL : It's just that German snow and Swiss snow look pretty much the same!

ROSENTHAL : Don't worry, there's a genuine man-made frontier right there, even though nature doesn't give a damn.

MARECHAL : I don't give a damn either. . . . *A pause.* And when the war's over, I'll come and get Elsa.

ROSENTHAL : Do you love her?

MARECHAL *sighing* : I guess I must!

ROSENTHAL *his hand on his friend's shoulder* : Remember, if we get across, you'll be going back to a squadron, and I back to a battery. We've got to fight again. . . .

MARECHAL *swearing* : We've got to finish this bloody war . . . let's hope it's the last.

ROSENTHAL : That's all an illusion! Come on, back to business. If we're seen by a patrol, what'll we do?

MARECHAL : Well, you run for it in one direction, and I in another . . . and it's each man for himself.

They are standing face to face now, seen from below.

ROSENTHAL : In case that happens, it might be safer to say our good-byes now . . . and see you soon.

They warmly embrace.

MARECHAL : So long, you bloody yid!

ROSENTHAL : Bye bye, old cheese!

Then side by side, they start running across the snow-

*covered fields towards the frontier. Pan to another area
of the mountain to show in a long shot from above, a
German patrol following the tracks of the two men.
Suddenly, a German soldier sees two black shapes in the
valley, about one hundred yards away. He makes a
gesture to the others, who aim their rifles and fire. (Still
on page 108) Cut to the two black shapes running.
Medium close-up of a German soldier starting to raise
his rifle again. The sergeant goes over to him and pushes
the muzzle of the rifle down. Both are seen from below as
they speak in German.*

THE SERGEANT: Don't shoot. They're in Switzerland!

The soldier puts the rifle in its sling on his shoulder.

THE SOLDIER: Lucky for them.

*Pan across the valley. Right at the bottom of the valley,
the two small shapes strain forward, sinking knee-deep in
the snow at every step. Cut to them walking away up the
snowy hillside.*